CW00349444

STOP SAVING THE NHS

...and start reinventing it

Colin Jervis

Kinetic Consulting

Published by
Kinetic Consulting Ltd.
Flat 8, Old Court
19c Montpelier Road
Ealing, London, W5 2QT

A catalogue record for this book is available for the British Library

ISBN 978-0-9576207-0-4 (Paperback)
ISBN 978-0-9576207-1-1 (eBook - Kindle)

Design by Brad Brooks @ Grafica by the Sea
Typeset in 11pt Minion Pro and Gotham Narrow

Printed by CreateSpace

Every reasonable effort has been made to ensure that the contents of this book are as accurate and as up-to-date as possible at the date of writing. However, the fields and topics addressed change continually; therefore neither the publisher nor the author is able to give any assurance that the content is complete, accurate and up-to-date. The information in this book is intended to be useful to a general reader and should not be used as a means of self diagnosis or for the prescription of medicine. Readers are urged to take advice from appropriately qualified medical practitioners in all cases. The publisher and author are not liable for any damages or negative consequences arising from the treatment, action or application of the information in this book to any person or organisation. Any references, including but not limited to authors, websites, books, products, manufacturers, organisations and individual practitioners, are provided for information only and not as an endorsement or approval.

CONTENTS

I must thank some people. First, my mother, who has supported me unrelentingly in whatever I have done and to whom I dedicate this book. Second, my reviewers, Andy Hadley, Peter Cook, Donatella Torsello, Helen Blanchard and Jeremy Holland.

FOREWORD

Soren Kierkegaard said life can only be understood backwards; but it must be lived forwards. Looking back on my working life, I can see that I have always worked closely with healthcare, whether in the public or private sectors. My work in the NHS began after a Master's degree and a change in career, a decision I made in a moment of epiphany, while watching a sunset from my London flat. Since then, I have worked in the NHS for about a total of ten years, in two stints, on both occasions leading multi-million pound Electronic Patient Record projects for two large hospitals. In the last ten years or so I have worked as a consultant, mainly, but not exclusively, to the health sector.

After the change of career, I became increasingly interested in the interplay of human dynamics with the implementation of large-scale IT systems. I was pleased to find that others were interested, including Professor Enid Mumford, whose work was a great influence. I was also influenced by Professor Peter Checkland's 'Soft Systems Methodology' which addresses soft problems that do not have a hard solution. It became increasingly clear to me that the implementation of large IT systems was rarely associated with improved returns—a problem that has engaged me for the last twenty years.

Healthcare seems to have lagged behind in realising that implementing IT did not change anything. Even when this insight was found, it was often addressed by an infelicitous mix of change management and training. In the main, the NHS has absorbed all investment in IT without changing its way of working. In fact, the direct patient benefits arising from NHS IT projects, including those schemes touted as successes, are difficult to find.

The simple truth is the NHS will not see significant improvements in care and improved efficiency until it creates new operational models with the support of fully-integrated Information Technology. Tinkering with, or automating, existing practice is nowhere near enough.

∼

Chapter 1: The Machine Stops summarises the challenges facing the NHS (and most healthcare systems in the developed countries) of a population that is becoming older, fatter and sicker—and one that is less inclined to accept the top-down delivery of traditional healthcare.

Chapter 2: The Promise of Genomics suggests that the decoding of the human genome has opened a huge potential for the planning, monitoring, diagnosis and delivery of healthcare. Furthermore, the binary codes of DNA base pairing and of computers have transformed Medicine into an information science.

Chapter 3: Other Developments mainly focuses on increasingly sophisticated and less expensive imaging technology that has made diagnosis easier and opened the way for a migration of healthcare from expensive institutions.

Chapter 4: Social Media looks at the phenomenon of social networking and how it might (and has already) affected the delivery of healthcare services.

Chapter 5: Human Touch and Computers looks at the strengths, weaknesses and potential of a man-machine partnership.

Chapter 6: Information Technology Can Save the NHS we arrive at the crux of the book where I suggest how the strengths of IT meet NHS needs; for example, a shared patient record; greater efficiency; managing structured healthcare and structured treatment.

Chapter 7: Digitising Medicine summarises the main elements of useful IT including chips, wireless, wireless tags, databases, patient records.

Chapter 8: Remote Care is now a reality and will develop further as newer sensors are produced. Pilot programs have shown it provides significant benefits for the aged and for those suffering from chronic illness.

Chapter 9: Remote Health Monitoring is also a reality and the smartphone could be a device on which to base that as well. Africa is making far more innovative use of the mobile phones than more developed continents.

Chapter 10: Robots Will Look After Us will robots be our helpers at home, doing the grunt work and being intelligent companions?

Chapter 11: IT as a Disruptor discusses how healthcare can escape from fixed thinking using IT to offer scalability, mutability and masses of data.

Chapter 12: Uneasy Past of the NHS and IT: despite the main theme, the NHS has been a reluctant adopter of IT and large programmes have foundered in the icy waters of resistance to change.

Chapter 13: Vision of Healthcare is a call to action and suggests how IT and operational change can be coupled to create a twenty-first century service.

FOR MORE INFORMATION

Please also visit *www.stopsavingthenhs.com* or *www.kineticconsulting.co.uk*. In addition, I post on Twitter about health and technology: *@colin_jervis.*

CHAPTER ONE

THE MACHINE STOPS

I have never forgotten the day Mr Walker read to my class from the beginning of E M Forster's *The Machine Stops*. At home that evening, I bolted down my dinner and lay on my bed devouring the rest of the story. Though written in Edwardian times, it is remarkably prescient, predicting television, video conferencing, and even remote-care and robotics. Forster describes a future where mankind lives underground in individual cells. All of its needs are met by the omnipresent Machine, which is regarded as a virtual deity.

Kuno is a ferret among the pallid, dependent and indifferent moles that his mother and the rest of humanity have become. Leaving his cell, he explores the tunnels outside, even making it to the surface before the Machine retrieves him. He sees what the rest do not: 'The Machine is stopping, I know it, I know the signs,' he tells his mother.

Forster said he wrote *The Machine Stops* as a reaction to one of the 'heavens' of the visionary H G Wells. Wells was a diabetic and in 1934 founded the UK Diabetes Society. He was also a proponent of universal healthcare, so he would have supported the creation of the UK's National Health Service—an omnipresent system to meet the health needs of the British people from cradle to grave.

And from cradle to grave the British have a love/hate relationship with the NHS. It rarely disappears from the news headlines—usually negative ones. Despite that, it has essentially seen off successive governments that have sought to reform it. And, for all of their carping, Britons still like its 'free at the point of care' principles.

But the NHS faces the greatest challenge since its formation. I know that has been said many times before, but this time it's true. Demographic changes, disruptive technologies, changed customer expectations and the stringencies of the post-credit-crunch world will vapourise its organisation, culture and practices...unless it adapts now.

DEMOGRAPHIC TRENDS

Two of the trends that will affect healthcare directly are an increased life expectancy and a falling birth rate.

During the twentieth century average life expectancy increased by about thirty years. In 1948 when the NHS was formed a male could expect to live to age sixty six. A male born today can expect to live until his late seventies. On average, women live about five years longer than men.

It is likely by 2026 twenty percent of the UK population will be over the age of sixty five. Projections also suggest that the number of people aged over eighty five will almost double between 2010 and 2026, rising from 1.2 to two million. Recent increases in fertility and immigration have slowed the ageing trend, but only a bit.

But *how* we age—and therefore how much care and support we need—is more important than how many aged people there are. The bad news is that demand for healthcare is set to increase sharply. The Department of Health estimates that by 2030 1.7 million more adults will need care and support. The effect of the ageing population is compounded, because there are fewer people of working age to pay for care and support. At present four people of working age support each pensioner; by 2035 this will fall to 2.5 and by 2050 to just two.

Birth rates have also fallen in the last thirty years. The birthrate in some European countries is as low as 1.2 children per family—far below the replacement level of 2.1. Birthrates in the UK have risen slightly recently with women having about 1.9 children, but this is far lower than the 2.93 in 1964.

Of course, these are only predictions made from a complex model that also needs to account for improved mortality rates and the effects of long-term conditions. Nonetheless, we must conclude that the NHS and social care are facing a rapidly-rising tide of demand.

OLDER, FATTER, SICKER

The longer we live the more we are likely to suffer from a chronic disease. Common chronic diseases include asthma, cancer, diabetes, coronary heart disease, high blood pressure as well as brain-wasting diseases like dementia and Parkinsonianism. The treatment of chronic disease consumes about seventy percent of NHS's resources accounting for about sixty-five percent of hospital bed days and about eighty percent of GP consultations.

Some diseases—like heart disease—can threaten life immediately; some, like diabetes, require intensive management; others, like arthritis, need care for a lifetime. Ironically, the prevalence of chronic disease has increased owing to increased life span and availability of better treatments.

A recent study in the Journal of Diabetic Medicine suggests the NHS spends £9.8 billion on the management of diabetes and predicted that by 2035 this would reach £16.8 billion—seventeen percent of the total NHS budget.

In the UK about 1.5 million people suffer from type 2 diabetes. Many go on to develop heart, kidney and vascular disease that may lead to limb amputation and some may go blind. Type 1 diabetes tends to appear in childhood and type 2 in later life. Both lead to problems in controlling the levels of blood sugar, and high levels over a long period can increase complications. For example, in men diabetes magnifies the risk of heart disease by two or three times; in women by two to four times.

About ten million people in the UK have arthritis and about 3.5 million have chronic obstructive pulmonary disease (COPD). Treating COPD alone costs £3.5 billion per year, and that does not account for lost working days and the misery the condition causes.

Furthermore, being overweight increases the likelihood of you suffering from a chronic disease. About sixty percent of adults and thirty percent of children in the UK are overweight and the trend is increasing. Worse, about twenty-five percent of adults are obese. Some experts say that obesity is a greater health risk than smoking and estimate at the current rate of growth three-quarters of the population could suffer the ill effects of obesity in fifteen years. The situation is so bad that many predict that the young will have a shorter life expectancy than their parents.

This state of affairs is exacerbated by the increasingly sedentary lifestyles that we lead. I know. Without making a special effort, I could easily spend the majority of my life in front of some screen or other: TV, PC, smartphone. Man the hunter/gatherer has become man the surf-and-clicker.

As the demands on social care and the NHS increase, the cracks between the various services become clearer. Many older or infirm people live in a triangle between social, primary and secondary care, often being passed between organisations in a macabre game of pass-the-patient. Silos of care are a real problem and lead us to ask why they should be here at all.

It is hard to escape from the conclusion that Britons are becoming older, fatter and sicker and will place an unprecedented load on the NHS. Indeed, some pundits believe the NHS is already close to breaking point.

MEDICAL KNOWLEDGE AND THE BALANCE OF POWER

Demographics and epidemiology are not the only challenges. Customers' expectations of service delivery have also changed. A couple of years ago I suffered months of excruciating stomach pain. I was prescribed proton pump inhibitors (PPI), but the discomfort worsened and I finally came to the conclusion that the PPIs were giving me constipation, so I stopped taking them.

I was eventually referred for an ultrasound scan that showed damage to my gall bladder, after which a consultant bundled me off with some over-the-counter remedies and told me the gall bladder would have to be removed if the symptoms persisted. During another painful, sleepless, night I did some internet research. Consequently, as a last resort, I asked my GP for antibiotics. Within a week of taking them the pain was gone and it hasn't returned since.

When the NHS was formed doctors transmitted information and patients received it. The doctor told the patient what to do and the patient did it. Those days are gone. Whatever doctors and the Department of Health may say about the risks of online self-diagnosis, the train has already left the platform. Nonetheless, I still hear reports of doctors' irritation when patients turn up with sheets printed from the internet. Wake up. Medical knowledge is no longer the domain of the few.

There is a wealth of information and diagnostic tools on the internet. A few hours of online research can give you enough knowledge to challenge the opinion of medical practitioners or at least to find the right questions to ask. I believe that you are the best person to look after your health. Moreover, as an informed customer able to challenge the Service, you are playing a part in creating twenty-first century healthcare.

Doctors with heads packed with information are no longer sufficient when patients have better, more up-to-date, and more reliable repositories of medical knowledge a click or a tap away. The balance of power between clinician and patient has shifted permanently.

Google knows more about us than our doctor. Search engines collect vast quantities of information about us, our activities and our preferences, and *Google* says that health-related searches are the second largest category. The information collected by search engines says a lot about our personality, interests and lifestyle that could be related to our general health. Unless we know our GP well, it is unlikely she would have available such comprehensive personal information.

It is supposed that medical diagnosticians carry about two million facts in their heads, but even doctors use the internet. Various research studies suggest doctors use search engines for health information. Engines like *Google Scholar* can also provide access to academic papers. Even two million facts are not enough when medical knowledge expands continually.

In 2006 the *British Medical Journal* reported a short study by Australian doctors that suggested that typing symptoms of unusual diseases into *Google* would lead to the correct diagnosis in fifteen out of seventeen cases. Indeed, useful information on even the most uncommon of diseases can be found on *Google* with a few mouse clicks.

Can *Google* replace the doctor? No way. Nonetheless, *Google's* usefulness is pointing the way. Moreover, misdiagnosis is still common among doctors despite better diagnostic tests and state-of-the-art scanning equipment. Studies of autopsies have shown doctors seriously misdiagnose fatal illnesses about twenty percent of the time.

MORE RESOURCES ARE NOT ENOUGH

In E M Forster's *The Machine Stops*, the mending apparatus fixes problems like an automated odd-job man. Its equivalent in the NHS has always been more cash, but now the challenge is so great not even that will sort it out. In 1948, when the NHS was launched, it had a budget of £437 million (about £9 billion in today's money). In 2010/11 it received more than ten times that amount. After accounting for inflation it has enjoyed roughly a four percent increase in funding per year.

In December 2010 a report by the National Audit Office: *Management of NHS Hospital Productivity* suggested unprecedented increases in funding have not led to unprecedented increases in productivity. Since 2000 spending has grown by two thirds and productivity has fallen year on year. With an increase in funding from £60 billion in 2000 to £102 billion in 2010 productivity fell by 1.4 percent per year.

Most of the recent funding increases have been absorbed by increases in salaries. Pay for doctors and nurses has increased by as much as sixty percent since 2000. However, productivity has not improved comparably. Increased pay has not increased patient appointments and procedures proportionately. The lauded increases in measured performance have come at a price.

More money has been spent on the NHS and output has increased but not in proportion. All machines and systems have a maximum level of performance. Once that level is reached, increasing inputs will not increase the level of performance. In fact evidence suggests that for every extra pound the public spends on the NHS, it gets less output. The only way to address this is to squeeze out additional efficiencies or to seek for a more effective system.

Increased funding has not taught the NHS to become more efficient, only how to spend more money. However, the credit crunch and the general economic downturn mean it must improve efficiency at the unprecedented rate of four to six percent a year to absorb increasing demand—even though its funding in real terms is to be maintained.

In this age of austerity and spending cuts, more funding seems unlikely. Moreover, even if more funds are found the evidence suggests they may not suffice. The mending machine of the NHS—like the one in E M Forster's short story—is failing.

Many are in denial. After all, the NHS has persisted and seen off more change initiatives than you can shake a ballot paper at. But the NHS deploys a limited range tactics to reduce spending. It cuts costs; rations treatment; top-slices funding; reduces services; and limits access to care (by whatever euphemism). These are typical reactions of an organisation unable to see past business-as-usual—and they will not suffice.

UNAFFORDABLE HEALTHCARE

In the West we have become used to improved living standards for the last fifty or more years. But there are concerns that the cost of healthcare is becoming unaffordable. Even before the recent cuts in public spending following the credit crunch, an EU study predicted that healthcare costs would increase by thirty-three percent by 2060—even after accounting for increased pension age, the reform of tax and benefits systems, and postulated increases in efficiency.

The NHS often defends itself against claims that it is inefficient by referring to international benchmarks against which it seems to represent value for money. However, the risk of benchmarking is that it gives a false sense of security and may simply compare obsolescent systems with one another. Later, we'll see the ways in which developing countries have been far more innovative with healthcare than Western countries— probably because they have no choice.

In *The Machine Stops* the trapped humans accept the Machine's defects, because the knowledge to repair it has been lost. Its service continues to deteriorate and the end is inevitable.

But constrained funds and fatter, older, sicker and better-informed consumers are not the only challenges the NHS faces. Technology, medical advances and changed expectations will challenge it even further.

SUMMARY

1. The UK population is aging. By 2026 twenty percent of the population will be over sixty-five. Demand for healthcare is also set to increase, and the Department of Health estimates an additional 1.7 million customers by 2030. A falling birth rate compounds the situation, because fewer people of working age will fund health-care through taxes.

2. An aging and overweight population is likely to suffer increasingly from long-term conditions such as asthma, diabetes, or coronary heart disease. These already account for about seventy percent of the cost of the NHS. For example, the NHS spends about £9.8 billion on the management of diabetes, and it is predicted this will rise to £16.8 billion by 2035.

3. Customers are readier to challenge clinical judgment and are no longer passive recipients, because they have access to vast stores of medical information on the internet.

4. Recent unprecedented increases in NHS funding have not been matched by increased efficiency, suggesting the current service has already passed its optimum working level. Seeking a more efficient NHS is not enough—we need a more effective system.

5. EU predictions suggest that healthcare is rapidly becoming unaffordable and that its cost could challenge Europe's already fragile economies.

6. Radical change is essential.

CHAPTER TWO

PROMISE OF GENOMICS

I first read about DNA (deoxyribonucleic acid) in James Watson's *Double Helix*. The unzipping of the two reversed strands interlocked by the strict pairing of nucleotides—as tightly choreographed as an episode of *Strictly Come Dancing* but far more consequential. Reading the book inspired me to study Biochemistry as an undergraduate, and I almost went on to a PhD in Molecular Biology.

In 2000 when the human genome code was cracked it revealed the biochemical code at the core of life and opened a jar of possibilities. We were shocked to discover that we had only about thirty to forty thousand genes, rather fewer than the 100 thousand that had been estimated, and we share about ninety-eight percent of our DNA with a chimpanzee and about fifty percent with a fruit fly—perhaps we're not as evolved as we might have assumed.

The genome is the overall blueprint at the core of the cell from which biochemical workers create new building blocks and metabolites. The genes coded on our DNA also determine our physical characteristics. If genes determine our future health and wellbeing, then decoding the human genome might be one of the most important advances in the planning, monitoring, diagnosis and delivery of healthcare.

DNA AND PROTEIN

DNA is rather like a spiral ladder in structure with the rungs being created by the pairing of components called bases. The four bases of DNA are adenine, thymine, cytosine and guanine—abbreviated to A, T, C, and G. They pair across the two strands of DNA in strict order: A pairs with T and G with C.

When the base pairs on the strands unzip, enzymes and other metabolites start constructing from the blueprint that is revealed. Three bases on a strand specify one amino acid; for example the sequences GGA, GGG, GGC, and GGU specify the amino acid, glycine.

Amino acids are the building blocks of protein, and about 100,000 proteins in the body control chemical reactions; contract muscles; transport oxygen and nutrients; maintain the body's balance; defend the body against infections; maintain the body's structure.

The sequence of amino acids determines the function of a protein and its three-dimensional structure. Therefore, changes can have a profound effect; for example changing one amino acid in the protein haemoglobin leads to it deforming and causing sickle-cell disease.

INHERITED DISEASE

Look at a photograph of Grigori Rasputin. Almost 100 years after his death those piercing eyes hypnotise. He was said to heal through prayer and developed a close relationship with Russia's, then ruling, Romanov family. The Tsarina Alexandra called on him every time the young Tsarevitch, who had haemophilia, was bleeding. Rasputin's mystical abilities seemed to revive the child even when doctors had given up.

Genetic inheritance, and specifically haemophilia, had a profound effect on European history in the nineteenth and twentieth centuries, and nowhere more so than in Russia, where the Romanovs' relationship with Rasputin brought them under severe criticism and probably hastened the downfall of the dynasty and ultimately the death of the whole family at the hands of the Bolsheviks.

The Tsarevitch was passed the haemophilia B gene by Queen Victoria, through her daughter, the Tsarina Alexandra. Similarly, it was passed to the ruling families of Spain, Germany and Russia to such an extent that it was referred to as the 'royal disease'. The gene manifests mainly in male descendants and can be inherited from a father or mother.

GENETIC TESTING AND PERSONALISED HEALTHCARE

The lure of the human genome is that the genes we inherit might be an indicator of our future health. For example, familial Alzheimer disease can be caused by the mutation of at least three genes: presenilin 1, presenilin 2 and amyloid precursor protein. This suggests genes may determine our health and also opens the possibility of genetic testing to support prophylaxis.

Testing is not new. Even before the human genome was decoded, tests could be carried out to determine foetal abnormalities such as Down's syndrome. On its own, genetic testing could allow propensity to about 6,000 inherited diseases— like haemophilia and sickle-cell anaemia—to be determined.

In 2007 James Watson was the second person to publish his genome online. He said: 'I am putting my genome sequence online to encourage the development of an era of personalised medicine, in which information contained in our genomes can be used to identify and prevent disease and to create individualised medical therapies'.

Human cells contain essentially the same genome, but they are differentiated when the DNA is read and converted into proteins. Errors occur during this process. There are point mutations—one base changed to another, and sometimes whole sections are deleted or new ones added. A mutation resulting in the change of one amino acid may cause a protein to adopt a different three-dimensional structure. This may trigger biological effects, some beneficial, some harmful.

Much is made of these differences, because they might allow our propensity to disease to be related to a genetic baseline. Small changes during a lifetime can lead to a person being prone to certain types of cancer or to suffering from a heart condition. Variations in DNA may also affect how we develop diseases and how we respond to drugs and vaccines.

A change in one base pair is named a Single Nucleotide Polymorphism or SNP. More than 53 million SNPs have been identified in humans. SNPs may lead to variation of the normal physiological pathways and the interaction between the various metabolites. However, most diseases seem to be multigenic with SNPs working together to manifest disease. Therefore, SNPs may be markers that allow personalised medicine to develop. Common patterns of SNPs may allow us to be stratified into groups and help us to manage our health and maybe predict the diseases to which we might be prone. Treatments could then be tailored for specific strata or groups.

EMPHASIS ON PROPHYLAXIS

Genetic typing could also move the emphasis of healthcare from disease management to disease avoidance—or at least disease mitigation. In support of that, it is thought that about 500 genes can be affected by exercise and lifestyle. So, by knowing what your risks are, you could adapt and prepare yourself for your likely future. This puts an informed patient in charge of their own health.

For example, metabolic syndrome is where someone with visceral-fat obesity has also developed two or more of the following: high blood pressure, high blood sugar or dyslipidaemia. High blood pressure and dyslipidaemia are called lifestyle-related diseases and are considered to be a result of poor diet or lack of exercise. Other lifestyle-related diseases include diabetes, cardiac infarction, brain infarction and cancer of the large intestine. Demographic studies suggest that gene mutations make a person more likely to develop lifestyle-related diseases.

Cancer may be a disease of the genome, therefore identifying its particular genetic fingerprint could allow a treatment to be targeted and to be more effective. Protein markers such as HER-2 (Human Epidermal Growth Factor Receptor 2) are an indicator of the effective use of the drug Herceptin in the treatment of cancer. So, rather than grouping cancers by location—breast, lung, prostate—we could group them by genetic marker. Drugs could then be developed for a particular target associated with that marker.

Too much medication is wasted. It is estimated that patient characteristics lead to forty percent of all medication failing to achieve the desired results or to side effects. Drugs amount to about ten percent of the total costs of care, so we are talking about large sums of money. Genomic targeting of drugs, so that the right drug is matched with the right patient, could reduce waste.

The Human Genome Project took ten years and cost billions of dollars. Today a genome can be sequenced in a day for around $4,000 and the cost it is expected to fall below $1,000 by 2014. In the UK about 700,000 children are born per year, and this raises the prospect of them all being presented with a copy of their genome at birth.

LIMITATIONS OF GENOMICS

That said, genetic mapping is probably at the peak of inflated expectations. Investment in molecular medicine research has increased sharply leaving traditional craft-based disciplines, like surgery, suffering from a reduction in funding. But no-one knows whether these expectations will be met. It all held great promise, but ten years on from the decoding of the human genome progress is not what might have been expected—though we would have to define what it was that we expected.

Further, if a car suffers a breakdown or an unexpected accident, we look first at the environmental conditions, the weather, the road conditions, the state of maintenance of the vehicle and even the performance of the driver. Our first recourse is not to look at the design of the car. Similarly, our health is likely to be affected by factors other than our genetic blueprint.

Lastly, testing people asymptomatically using genomics presents ethical problems—even if giving your child a copy of their genome at birth seems attractive. So predictive testing may be limited to consenting adults, at least to begin with.

PROTEONOMICS AND EPIGENETICS

We have about 30,000 genes, but there are about 100,000 proteins. The interaction between these biological players—planned or accidental—is likely to have a more profound effect on our health than our overall design. So, for example, the discipline of Proteomics focuses on fingerprint proteins that also might detect our propensity to disease.

It is generally accepted that we are products of our genes and our environment—nature and nurture. One unchange-able, the other subjective according to experiences, influences and the pressure of life. But new research suggests genes can change. Identical twins who share genetic material can be completely different. The new science of Epigenetics suggests that genes can be switched on and off, and the effect of nurture might be passed on. Studies in China and the US over a century ago show famines affected lifespan and obesity. Lack of food activated genes that increased body fat to improve survival. Therefore, they may have triggered the obesity crisis that we now face.

We will see if Molecular Medicine lives up to its promise. Even the exquisite DNA translation process sometimes gets it wrong and proteins end up with the wrong amino acids. Indeed the majority of DNA itself is regarded as 'junk', because it seems to have no function. To me this seems rather like computer code and its creation, and there is a growing relationship between the two.

MEDICINE AS AN INFORMATION SCIENCE

I worked in international marketing for a while and travelled the world. I was always proud (and grateful!) that English is the most widely-spoken language with about eighty percent of the world being able to speak it. But it is not the real *lingua franca* any more. The most popular language comprises 0s and 1s—the binary language of computers. G B Shaw said America and England were 'separated by the same language,' but the binary language unites the world. And the binary language of DNA is the strict base pairing: A to T and G to C. Information seems to be at the core of life and these two binary languages are set to dominate medicine in the coming decades.

Bioinformatics is at the intersection of computer science and molecular biology. Its aim is to bring together biological knowledge and use that to develop new knowledge and derive insights about living systems. Given my attraction to the code of life and to computer code, if I was going to university now I might be attracted by this, because it lies at the convergence of genomics and computer science, or of man and machine—rather like the overall theme of this book.

The possibilities opened when computing power is combined with molecular biology are many. What's more, research into this area goes beyond the confines of a laboratory and becomes an information science. For example, if I discover a new protein, I can check online databases and from that infer all sorts of information from accumulated knowledge.

This also raises the prospect of molecular structures being created and transferred digitally to where they can be constructed; for example, imagine creating molecular models of vaccines that could be quickly distributed to tackle pandemics.

Machine and biological languages can be combined to create what is essentially an information science that deals with vast amounts of data about human behaviour and health. IT combined with advances in genetics creates the ultimate disruptive technology and the prospect of proactive health-care. I have been fascinated by the interface between man and machine for more than thirty years. Now it seems more alluring than ever.

SUMMARY

1. Cracking of the human genome might be the most important advance in the planning, monitoring, diagnosis and delivery of healthcare.

2. DNA has four important components called bases: adenine, thymine, cytosine and guanine—abbreviated to A, T, C, and G. Across the two intertwined strands of DNA, bases pair in strict order: A with T and G with C.

3. During replication the two strands unwind and the triplets of bases that are revealed are code for individual amino acids. Amino acids are the components of proteins—which are the building blocks of human physiology.

4. Some diseases, like haemophilia, are transmitted by inheritance, as are our main characteristics. Therefore, our genes may predict our health and may allow our propensity to certain diseases to be anticipated, opening the possibility of personalised healthcare.

5. The cost of decoding an individual genome has decreased from £billions to about £1,000, creating the possibility of children being given a copy of their genome at birth as a sort of health map.

6. We have about 30,000 genes but more than 100,000 proteins, so it is likely the molecular story does not end with genes. Ten years after the decoding of the human genome, Genomics is at the peak of inflated expectations.

7. Small changes in the structure of DNA called Single Nucleotide Polymorphisms (SNPs) may allow

populations to be stratified and the groupings used to assess our future health and the likely effectiveness of treatments.

8. The binary DNA base pairings, A to T and G to C, when combined with the binary computer language used by computers, form a disruptive technology that has transformed medicine into an information science.

CHAPTER THREE

OTHER DEVELOPMENTS

When Thomas Roentgen took an x-ray of his wife's hand she exclaimed: 'I have seen my death!'. But his discovery has led to life for many. Medicine has been transformed by imaging equipment such as CT (Computed Tomography), PET (Positron Emitted Tomography) and MRI (Magnetic Resonance Imagery) that allow our bodies to be viewed with unprecedented clarity using computer constructs.

Most of us are familiar with ultrasound scanning through its use to assess foetal development in pregnant women. It uses high-frequency sound waves to generate an image of the inside of the body. Because it uses sound, rather than radiation, the procedure is relatively safe. It can also be used to examine internal organs, such as the liver, kidneys and abdomen, and even further to assess physiological functions like blood flow and the functioning of the heart.

CT uses computing and x-rays to create cross-sectional images of the human body. Cross sections can then be assembled to create a complex image. Recently it has been used in preventative medicine, for example CT colonography for patients with a high risk of colon cancer, and some organisations offer a full body scan as a preventative check, though the usefulness of this is debatable.

MRI uses a magnetic field to align the magnetic fields of atoms in the body. Radio frequencies systematically alter this alignment, which produces a rotating magnetic field that is detected by a scanner and used to create an image. It can be used to produce precise three-dimensional images of joints and soft tissue. Scans contrast different soft tissue, making them useful for imaging the brain, muscles, the heart and cancers.

A specialised type of MRI, named Functional Magnetic Resonance Imaging (fMRI) measures changes in blood flow, related to neural activity in the brain and spinal cord and is one of the most recent forms of neuro-imaging. It can be applied, for example, to measuring activity in the brain.

PET tracks radioactively labelled substances to measure the metabolism and the distribution of metabolites. It is often used with CT scans to create a more precise picture.

Multiple CT, MRI and ultrasound scans can be combined by software to produce three-dimensional images. These images can then be manipulated and are a great resource in the identification and treatment of many diseases. Such images allow surgeons to 'travel' up the internal channels, like nerves, blood vessels and the digestive system.

EFFECT OF MEDICAL IMAGING

Medical imaging offers greater accuracy of diagnosis and clearer internal views and suggests the possibility of diagnoses and procedures being carried out by less-skilled and less-specialised staff. Moreover, devices are becoming more compact and less expensive. For instance, the average cost of an ultrasound device is falling. From £57,000 in 2000 it is expected to fall soon to £3,000. This opens the real prospect of sophisticated imaging devices—and therefore the diagnosis and procedures that go with them—being located outside of large institutions, perhaps in local clinics.

The other main effect, often overlooked because it is so obvious, is that digital images are easily shared promoting greater sharing and co-operation among clinicians—even in real time—no matter where they are located or in which organisation. This is a simple but important step in the migration to a new vision of healthcare.

ROBOTIC SURGERY

In an interview on BBC Radio 4 in August 2008, Lord Winston, a well-known UK media figure in medicine, debated the future of robots in healthcare with Professor Noel Sharkey. Lord Winston concluded that patients need human contact and the healing touch, so robotics would never catch on. But human contact and robotic precision are not mutually exclusive. They can be compatible—even a team.

In future, one of the key indicators of a prospective surgeon may be their dexterity at computer games, as computer precision and imaging combine. Virtual reality uses computer simulation to create a lifelike experience. Mostly this is visual, but may include other sensory information like sound and even movement. Further, haptic feedback, which aims to simulate the feel of a procedure, holds the promise of adding a greater sense of touch—sensors mimicking touch and feel of, say, a scalpel cutting. The top guns of surgery may also be the top gun wielders in shoot-'em-up games. They are, of course, a combination of human skill and machine simulation—rather in the same way that sophisticated jet fighters are controlled.

Computer simulation is being adopted into medical education, allowing students to practice without risk. More powerful computers, high definition graphics and higher-speed data communications are making virtual reality increasingly lifelike. Further, the cost of virtual reality is falling, particularly in the wake of the burgeoning games industry. It is set to be widely adopted in the next decade and is yet another mechanism by which skills will be transferred in coming decades.

NANOTECHNOLOGY

The 1966 movie *Fantastic Voyage* has a miniaturised submarine, the *Proteus*, navigating the internal channels of an unconscious scientist to destroy a clot in his brain. Nanotechnology aspires to create new manufacturing processes and machines using atoms as the building blocks. Among other things, Nanotechnology seeks to create similar miniaturised do-gooders, like in the movie, to diagnose, prevent and treat disease. Tiny nano-particles, could, for example, carry a tiny bullet of drug direct to a cancerous cell, thereby limiting the collateral damage caused by the scattergun of chemotherapy.

The success of this technology lies in materials research, specifically in biocompatibility and nanotechnology. Nanobots operate in biological environments, including tissue, blood, acids and other bodily fluids. They must remain functional in these hostile environments while not causing an immune or adverse reaction in the patient. In Fantastic Voyage, for example, the crew has to fight off an attack by engulfing white blood cells.

Of course, there are plenty of other promising advances; for example, monoclonal antibodies and the development of vaccines—note how quickly a vaccine was developed the H1N1 flu virus—but they fall outside the scope of this book and don't significantly change my argument.

Technology and IT are helping to make medicine cheaper, reproducible and smaller in scale—as well as encouraging improved communications. Overall, they support a move to decentralisation and automation of diagnosis, intervention and treatment.

SUMMARY

1. Imaging technologies like CT and MRI use computing to create images of the human body of exceptional quality which allow, for example, interior views of the digestive and nervous systems.
2. The cost of imaging devices is falling, so that sophisticated diagnosis does not depend on a large budget and can migrate from large institutions.
3. Robotic surgery shows that machines and humans can work together. Surgeons of the future may be those adept at playing computer games.
4. Other exciting technologies are developing, for example, nanotechnology and monoclonal antibodies.

CHAPTER FOUR

SOCIAL MEDIA

Maria and I had been comparing the music collections on our smartphones but, being generations apart, frankly, we didn't have much in common. So the topic of conversation switched. She was concerned. The whole of her life was on *Facebook* she told me—all of her photographs and many of the experiences of her young (twenty-two years) of life, stored and recorded there. She feared that all might be lost if something happened to the online storage.

The millennial generation seems to have been born with a mobile phone and a *Facebook* page that their parents had already staked out for them. *Facebook* has one billion users who share experiences, photographs and sometimes more intimate details of their lives with an international audience of friends and friends of friends. Access through the Web, or using a mobile phone, make this a continual necessity for many young people—with some older people not far behind in enthusiasm.

Facebook recently floated on the stock market with a market capitalisation of $100 billion—quite a price for a piece of software and a database of user information. Most of the assumed value is in user goodwill, and the share price has fallen recently as investors begin to wonder how that user database and user goodwill can be converted into a sweating, income-generating asset.

Nonetheless, one billion users is an awful lot. So rather than worrying about shareholder value, we should look at how the *Facebook* phenomenon has affected user behaviour and expectations specifically with respect to healthcare.

Of course, *Facebook* is not the only social medium. Blogging is another way of expressing your feelings, experiences and opinions. We also have *Twitter*, a microblogging site that allows you to post short message about what you are doing and to interact with people whom you follow or who follow you.

I started blogging about eight years ago. Then 'real' journalists regarded it with disdain. How things have changed! Now the Web, *Twitter* and blogging are part of the mainstream of journalism and the traditional media scramble to keep up with the posts of people on the spot at events like the demonstrations in Tahrir Square in Cairo that toppled an Egyptian presidency.

ONLINE IS FOREVER

Once upon a time you went to an Indian restaurant with a group of friends and at the end of the evening would be a curry stain on a tablecloth and some pleasant recollections. Now, social interaction is no longer so ephemeral. No longer is it a fleeting impression of body language or a partly understood comment that is lost forever. Social interactions—word and image—are now recorded online, permanently.

What's more, the dividing line between private and public has been redrawn. NHS customers now share large sections of their lives with the world and store it electronically. It's all there: interactions, interest groups, support groups, friends, unfriends, activities, photographs, videos. Let's face it, the record on *Facebook* is more detailed, intimate and accurate than the medical records maintained by our GP and the rest of the NHS.

SHARING INTIMATE DETAILS

Recording your life and sharing it with your friends is one thing, but how about making the most intimate details of an illness available to all?

Jeff Jarvis on his *Buzz Machine* blog wrote about his prostate cancer, which was diagnosed in 2009. He told the world about his choice of robotic surgery and subsequently about the malfunctioning of his private bits and his need to wear an adult nappy. Two years later, we read about his use of Viagra and Cialis to treat his impotence—which only gave him indigestion.

Some may think this too much information, but Jarvis is a champion of online openness and of living the intimate details of his life in public. He believes such openness enriches human knowledge by providing a shared resource, and he thinks people who keep such information confidential could be regarded as selfish.

CLINICIAN AND PATIENT POWER

The internet is responsible in large part for a migration in attitude in the NHS from patrician to advisor. Power can be maintained by control over resources and information. The latter control has gone, because medical knowledge is online for everyone.

Therefore, the balance of power in the clinical patient relationship has also shifted. Patients are no longer passive recipients and go online to assess their own conditions and to find out more about them—particularly if they feel a doctor did not give them enough information.

Patients are now active consumers of healthcare, which means they will seek information, comparisons and the opinions of others in the same way as they do when booking a hotel or buying a new washing machine.

HEALTHCARE SOCIAL MEDIA MISMATCH

The *Facebook* generation and the explosion of social media are adding to the pressure on the NHS, because they create an expectation of personal-service delivery.

Social networks are based on openness and transparency, but parts of the NHS struggle with this, and the tendency is still is to give a patient only what a practitioner wants her to know. On *Facebook* I share information with friends in Thailand, Australia and Milton Keynes and gain a fast response. An NHS hospital in Milton Keynes would have trouble in transferring my information to the right people in Milton Keynes, let alone meeting any expectation of fast response. Social media are more comprehensive and combine text, voice and images with ease. I can also connect by video link to my friends and share information with them before, during and after an event.

What's more, on *Facebook* I can stop the sharing immediately by 'unfriending'. Try something similar in the NHS. Whatever I choose to share—some or all on *Facebook*—it is *me* that decides what and with whom, not some middleman. This is quite a contrast to the disparate and infelicitous mixture of paper and electronic records held by the NHS.

NHS records are becoming more secure. Nonetheless, paper records are regularly lost, left in corridors, or forgotten in the boots of cars. Unscrupulous journalists can (and have) bribed unscrupulous employees to make copies of records in whatever form they were held. Further, I have personal experience of a GP having 'lost' several years of my electronic record, and I have lost track of the number of times I have been able to read confidential information on monitors at clinic reception desks.

However, old ideas about confidentiality are eroding. Too often powerful groups use the confidential nature of the patient-clinician relationship as a reason for refusing to make progress—particularly in the sharing of patient records. However, in the world of social media we have seen that Jeff Jarvis promotes extreme openness in his clinical affairs, because he believes it adds to the store of human knowledge. I don't suggest all of us will wish to share the details of our health with everyone, but I do think social media are promoting greater openness.

SOCIAL VALIDATION AND EXPERT OPINION

Social networks revolve around social validation where it is important to fit in and to share the values of a group. Despite recent movements to patient partnership and advocacy, the NHS still maintains a top-down patrician culture based on the expertise of a few people. This suggests a greater role for more empathic support and for learning and communication—fitting well with the work of social care and the management of chronic conditions and the elderly.

In summary, the NHS looks more and more like an analogue anachronism that will increasingly grate with the digital world. Social media are by design paper free, electronic, connected, multi-media and, most of all, open. The NHS is firmly mired in paper on islands of compliance.

TURNING HEALTHCARE INSIDE OUT

The NHS has also been opened to greater public scrutiny and even censure by social media. The majority of NHS staff are committed and well meaning, but like any large organisation it has a particular culture, and it employs a few oddballs. Consequently, portrayals of hospital life on popular, fictional TV shows like *Holby City* are being challenged by some social media realities.

Many instances have been reported of the posting of patient information and photographs on social media. A member of my family has personal experience of a nurse posting pictures of patients on her ward on *Facebook*—interlaced with derogatory comments about clinical managers.

In September 2011 newspapers reported the social media antics of NHS doctors who debated openly on *Twitter* which wards were the worst to work on. Cabbage patches—intensive care units for post-CBG (Coronary Bypass Graft) patients—rated highly. But Maternity units or 'birthing sheds' as they called them and the 'madwives' who worked in them were deemed worse. Now, doctors are not the first to have posted unwisely on social media. Politicians and policemen and many other groups have also been caught out, and the doctor concerned eventually apologised. Still, you have to wonder how many private-sector employees would have kept their jobs after being so disparaging of their colleagues and customers.

Online interactions and customer opinions make it possible for consumers of NHS services to make up their own minds about exactly how 'passionate' (or substitute the current shibboleth) about patient care an NHS organisation really is.

HOW THE NHS IS USING SOCIAL NETWORKING

The reaction of health professionals to this shift is varied. Some still feel threatened and want to assert their professional dominance; the more enlightened collaborate with the patient and seek to assess the information he has found and guide him to reliable sources.

As an organisation the NHS has responded in a variety of disconnected ways to the popularity of social media. Some NHS organisations use it as a broadcast medium or as another means of communicating; for example, by responding to individual requests using *Twitter*. Some trusts have their own social media sites; for example, University College London Hospitals has a *Twitter* and *Facebook* site. My impression is that NHS use for communication, or as an attempt to further engage, has been only moderately successful—at least to judge by levels of interaction.

The Department of Health has set up an online rating service on its flagship *NHS Choices* site that allows patients to rate their GPs. Patients can comment on how easy it was to get an appointment, upload comments about the service and indicate whether they would recommend the practice to others. The Department of Health says that this will give patients the information they need to choose between England's 8,000 GP practices.

This is a start, but really what I want to know is how good the service is when measured against some benchmark. Also, patient comments are useful, but ultimately subjective. What I also really want to know is how good is a practice at its main function—which is keeping its patients healthy.

With broadcast, communications and to some extent engagement, the NHS is making progress with social media, but other organisations are taking it much further, much faster.

HOW OTHER HEALTHCARE ORGANISATIONS ARE USING SOCIAL MEDIA

Diabetes UK is a not-for-profit organisation that uses the Web, *Facebook* and *Twitter*. On *YouTube* you can also watch videos made by fellow diabetics and hear about research and the latest treatments. It has more than 20,000 members and more than 100,000 people have assessed their risk of contracting type 2 diabetes using an online tool. The Stroke Association and the Coeliac Society have similar online presences.

It is significant that social media that are personalised to particular conditions, and encourage real interaction, are popular. In the future, chronically ill patients may be able use online social networks to complement their NHS treatment. You can also foresee them being used for bringing together groups with similar genetic characteristics, like the SNPs I talked about earlier, that could be used to stratify and associate them with regimes of healthcare.

PATIENTS LIKE ME

On the social networking site *PatientsLikeMe* members share information about their medical conditions. They post about their treatment, symptoms, experiences and general mood. The site organises user information graphically so patients can spot patterns and trends thereby gaining greater insight into their conditions. It also aims to help patients to improve outcomes with the support of fellow sufferers.

Two of the site's founders have a brother who was diagnosed with Amyotrophic Lateral Sclerosis (ALS)—which was also the condition on which the site was founded. But it now has communities for HIV, fibromyalgia, multiple sclerosis, Parkinson's disease and more. It has more than 100,000 members.

PatientsLikeMe has tried a new way of assessing drug effectiveness based on patient reports and using tools on the site. In May 2012 the *Lancet Neurology* reported on tests of the drug Lithium. Site members suffering from ALS began taking the drug after a small trial suggested it could inhibit the progress of the disease. The trial on the site arrived at a similar conclusion to the journal study but at a far lower cost. While this approach may not replace conventional trials, it has the virtue of investigating the real-world effects on patients with multiple morbidities who might otherwise be eliminated from conventional trials.

REALITY MINING AND BIG DATA

When Florence Nightingale went to manage the care of injured soldiers in the Crimean War she complained that 'in scarcely an instance have I been able to obtain hospital records fit for any purposes of comparison.' A cynic might suggest 200 years after her death we have a lot more records but scarcely more information. The NHS collects huge numbers of data to report to all and sundry, and particularly to report against performance targets.

When I first started to work in healthcare, pundits claimed the NHS was data rich and information poor. We have plenty of information on what the NHS does—its processes—but far less on how effective it is. When I go into a health system unwell, essentially I want to come out feeling better. That is the outcome I seek. But it seems outcome has been redefined to mean process, perhaps so that it will not silence a room full of clinicians if uttered at an inconvenient moment.

These days our activities leave a trail of digital breadcrumbs—many loaves-worth each day. From the wireless devices we use; from GPS; from credit card payments; from our interactions on the internet social networks. These breadcrumbs combine to give a detailed picture of our lives.

Reality mining could use these digital breadcrumbs to predict things like the spread of disease or how our daily activity relates to our health. Also, a mixture of genetic profiles and reality mining could collect structured information about the health of people in the UK, building a database of information that could occupy researchers for decades.

Big Data is a related idea. It can be collected from web logs, social networks, internet use, search engines, genomics, video, photographs and CCTV. I once listened to a professional biographer lamenting the demise of letter writing, which meant she had less information to research, but in fact more of our life is permanently recorded than ever.

CHANGING EXPECTATIONS

Social networks influence customer expectations about the way in which services should be delivered, and the NHS has some way to go before it can meet those expectations. Other healthcare organisations have created support groups that could form the basis of future care and research, particularly for those suffering from chronic conditions.

The NHS exhibits a variety of responses to social media from broadcast, through communication, to comparison, to group creation. It is unclear to me that the NHS has yet grasped social media for what they really are—forums for interaction and conversation where openness is a crucial factor.

Social networks create a hive that can support and guide, but that can also generate a wave of public opinion. So, we can expect new treatments and services to go viral quickly and for social opinion to quickly drive healthcare delivery.

But there's much more. Combine *Facebook* with the opportunities for personalisation and group creation afforded by people sharing similar genetic characteristics and a new dimension opens. Here, then, is the potential to engage consumers and to recruit them as true partners in a revised form of care.

SUMMARY

1. Social media are a global phenomenon that supports interaction on a scale and at a pace that has left traditional media behind. *Facebook*, though only eight years old, has one billion users.

2. Social media have redrawn the line between public and private. Users share intimate details of their lives with friends whom they choose. Details of social interaction can be stored online forever. Some people have even shared the intimate details of illness online.

3. Accordingly, social validation will become an important factor in healthcare delivery. People will seek the opinions of others about services. New services, drugs and treatments are likely to 'go viral' quickly.

4. The NHS is still developing its use of social media. Nonetheless, *NHS Choices* allows patients to express their opinions of services, including 8,000 GP practices.

5. Sites that concentrate on specific conditions like diabetes and coeliac disease have a greater degree of openness and interaction, perhaps because of the cohesion created by a greater focus and greater empathy.

6. *Patientslikeme* is a website specialising on supporting specific conditions that has also promoted the use of its site for use in clinical trials. Its users are more representative of the general patient population.

7. Digital interactions, such as activity on the Web and mobile phones generate vast quantities of data about our activities, sometimes called Big Data they can also be

used in Reality Mining and could be related to research into healthcare and epidemiology.

8. The user facilities and characteristics of social media, such as speed, openness and personalisation, create an expectation of service delivery that the NHS will struggle to equal.

CHAPTER FIVE

HUMAN TOUCH AND COMPUTERS

'Mind, that was a parcel,' said my mother. We were just leaving the Queens Cinerama in Newcastle-upon-Tyne having sat through Stanley Kubrick's film *2001 a Space Odyssey*. Though my mother was unimpressed, it is now held as a cinematic classic, and the omniscient computer HAL 9000 as one of its most memorable characters.

OK, so owing to a programming conflict, HAL sabotaged the ship and killed all but one of the crew—but, hey, no-one's perfect. But before all of that, it worked with the crew, monitored the ship as it headed on its mission to Jupiter, and carried out routine maintenance—it was even programmed to lose to the crew at chess occasionally—a man/machine partnership.

Yet here we are well past 2001 and computers have still not achieved the omniscience of HAL. Nonetheless, they are omnipresent. The microchip is in our homes, in our cars, at our work and in our pockets, and there are some developments in machine intelligence that will change medical practice for good.

DOCTORS AND MEDICAL KNOWLEDGE

Spot a junior doctor in a hospital by her white coat, dog-eared *British National Formulary* in the right pocket, dog-eared *Oxford Textbook of Medicine* in the left and a stethoscope slung about her neck. She arrives at her first real job having memorised the nervous system, anatomy, physiology, biochemistry, and she will be asked to recognise and manage a shed-load of ailments that share a handful of similar symptoms.

Doctors leave medical school knowing about sixty drugs. There are about 3,000 in the formulary of most acute hospital systems—and let's leave aside possible interactions between them, which spawns a combinatorial explosion of information doctors are expected to remember and to juggle in their memory—and daily the number of drugs and conditions increases.

It is also sobering to consider that about seventy percent of prescribing in acute hospitals is done by pre-registration or first-year doctors. Many of them also transcribe drug charts from the handwritten glyphs of senior doctors. These are sometimes so illegible that junior doctors resort to tracing handwriting. I wish I was joking.

DIAGNOSIS AND HOUSE

This reality is in sharp contrast to the portrayal of Dr Gregory House of the HBO TV series *House*. He is a brilliant, misanthropic curmudgeon who likes to avoid contact with patients. For him, the thrill is in solving the puzzle, rather than helping the patient. He ignores rules, medical ethics and authority. He manipulates his staff, insults patients and cheats his friends. Basically, he's a sociopath—less murderous than HAL 9000 perhaps—but a poorer chess player with less well-developed social skills.

The role of diagnostician remains one of the most challenging and fulfilling roles of a doctor. Doctors are estimated to carry two million facts in their heads to fulfill this role. In making a diagnosis they are expected to use all of their knowledge and apply it to the patient and situation in front of them, carrying out differential diagnosis by juggling half a dozen possible diagnoses in their brain until they find one which best fits the symptoms.

Does it work? Most of the time. Studies of post mortems have shown that doctors misdiagnose fatal diseases in about twenty percent of cases.

DIAGNOSIS AND *GOOGLE*

I was with friends in a pub debating the word for fear of open spaces: is it acro- or agoraphobia? I won the five pound bet on the spot, using my smartphone to confirm it on the Web. Though I was confident of my answer through years of learning and education, there is less need these days to store large numbers of facts in your head, unless you want to take part in a TV quiz—or be a doctor.

Frankly, there are better ways of storing two million facts. Search engines offer instant access to vast knowledge bases. *Google* accesses more than three billion articles on the web, which surpasses more traditional academic search engines. It is the medium of choice for retrieving medical articles, and *Google Scholar* is likely to be even more useful as it searches only peer-reviewed articles.

In 2006 a study in the *British Medical Journal* suggested that difficult-to-diagnose illnesses could be inferred by a

Google search. Three to five search terms were entered for twenty-six notoriously difficult-to-diagnose illnesses, including Cushing's syndrome and Creutzfeldt-Jacob disease. The study found Google was right in about fifty-eight percent of the cases—though interpretation of the search results did rely on specialised knowledge.

Another US study in 2011 by Wolters Kluwer Health, suggested about forty-six percent of doctors used *Google* frequently and another thirty-two percent admitted to using it as an occasional resource. My experience suggests that junior staff use it more frequently than this—many using online resources to calculate drug dosages, for example.

INTUITION

But doctors know they are not search engines and much is made of medical intuition. Einstein was a great champion of intuition, yet his discovery of the Special Theory of Relativity came after years of hard thought during which he almost drove himself mad. Is that calculation or intuition? Does intuition exist, or is a function of our prejudices and biases, like our tendency to make up our minds about people in a few seconds?

Despite claims that human intuition is better than raw calculating power, the evidence is ambivalent. Tests at Yale University in the 1970s suggested that intuitive thinkers arrived at conclusions more quickly, but the level of accuracy did not differ from that of non-intuitive thinkers.

Medical intuition seems to come as a consequence of years of experience and is dependent on a doctor having encountered the same collection of symptoms and the same disease before. Knowledge of this type is expensive to procure.

Intuition seems to be like the Yeti: many believe it to exist, but few claim to have seen it. But if intuition is related to our human ability to notice small indicators unconsciously, maybe it is better related to empathy than a mechanical rational process and, therefore, will become a skill more in demand as computers take over the calculation and storage functions of doctors.

Doctors are intelligent, but I have met none with a ten ton brain. Is there still a need for the prodigious feat of memory that they have to undertake at medical school? Online data bases can hold all of that information and more and it can also be updated easily. We seem to expect doctors to be a mobile array of sensors and a repository of information with an inference engine attached. Does that sound like work for a human in the digital age? It sounds more like a machine to me.

ARTIFICIAL INTELLIGENCE AND COMPUTERS

The possible positions in the game of chess outnumber the atoms in the universe and the game has often been used as a standard for intelligence. These days chess computers are a match for all but the very best players. In the film *Kasparov vs the Machine*, Garry Kasparov—still the most highly rated chess player ever until very recently—is seen losing to IBM's *Deep Blue* computer.

In raw calculating power, machines already exceed us, and they do so without emotional baggage. Machines do not get upset, fight with their partners, or turn up late with a hangover. In fact, anyone who watched *Kasparov vs the Machine* might conclude that he defeated himself by becoming suspicious and then upset about the implications of *Deep Blue's* erratic play. Had he played his normal game, he may have won.

Two luminaries with two different approaches have led the search for an independent-thinking machine, like HAL 9000. Doug Lenat began *Cyc* in 1984. It is not a robot, but rather a knowledge-base of fundamental information: facts, rules-of-thumb and heuristics for learning about objects and everyday life. *Cyc* is intended to normalise and minimise the amount of knowledge needed to develop common sense. When it has attained this basic level, it will be ready to tackle more complex problems, like the processing of natural language.

On the other hand, Rodney Brooks of Massachusetts Institute of Technology's Artificial Intelligence lab has taken a different approach to machine learning. *Cog* learns about the world through its senses by using eye, head and hand. By creating a humanoid robot and allowing it human experiences, researchers believe robots are more likely to develop brains and capabilities similar to ours.

Recently IBM's supercomputer *Watson* has been applied to assisting doctors in diagnosis. *Watson* attempts to understand natural language and then access unstructured information to look for a correspondence between a patient's record and medical literature. It then presents the information and its inferences ranked by likelihood.

$\sim$

EXPERT SYSTEMS WILL SUPPORT
HUMAN PRACTITIONERS

In well understood domains, like chess, computers can exceed humans at calculation. Therefore, once the diagnosis and treatment of a disease has become standardised and codified, human practitioners are unlikely to be able to compete with the same level of precision and accuracy. In this respect, one area of Artificial Intelligence that has shown promise is Expert Systems. These seek to encode both human knowledge and the rules-of-thumb that doctors and other experts routinely use to short-cut their thinking.

An Expert System often includes a user interface, an inference engine and an underlying knowledge base. So in the context of a doctor's brain, the user interface faces the patient and gathers information. The inference engine contains the workings of the brain whose connections are laid by training and years of experience. It is where the rules-of-thumb are gleaned and derived. The underlying knowledge base contains the medical information; conditions; symptoms; guidelines; diagnostic test ranges; drugs and their interactions.

It is easy to see Expert Systems being used in routine medicine—triage, for example. But as medicine becomes increasingly codified and commoditised their scope will increase. Perhaps the most practical application will be in medical care. For example, at present if you feel ill, you may have to wait hours in an emergency waiting room before you see a doctor. In the near future, you may simply be able to consult an Expert System.

The company Infermed produces an inference engine named *Arezzo*. It uses best practice, guidelines and probability to recommend a pathway of care. It supports a clinician in diagnosis and treatment by using best practice, probability and guidelines—such as those issued by the National Institute for Clinical Excellence (NICE) in the UK.

Arezzo has three main components: *Composer* that allows guidelines to be entered; *Tester* a guideline testing tool; and *Performer* that runs guidelines at the point of care. For example, to assess the risk of cardiovascular disease, doctors are prompted to ask a series of questions, examine the patient and take a blood sample. A doctor can select appropriate assessment routes. So if she suspects cancer, the correct diagnostic pathway is selected which may conclude with a recommendation to, say, refer, carry out further tests, or wait and see. Assessments are given with the relevant consequences on the course recommended.

Doctors can add notes to pathways that can be used to improve the general knowledge base. This could increase the accuracy of diagnosis; reduce inappropriate referrals; and decrease the variability in care. It can also act as a communication tool to spread best practice. It is easy to see how such a system could be used by less qualified staff to help them to reach feasible and evidence-based diagnoses.

NHS Direct has been offering telephone support to NHS patients since 1997. Since using *Arezzo* it claims to have saved 1.3 million visits to other healthcare organisations, including 0.7 million fewer to GPs, which, it says, saved the NHS £57 million.

COMPUTERIZED COGNITIVE BEHAVIOUR THERAPY

While researching for a MBA dissertation I came across an expert system called *ELIZA* that did little more than ask reflective questions—for example: 'Tell me more about...' or 'What do you mean by...?'. Nonetheless, many patients consulting it responded positively. One woman left in tears after a consultation saying she had never before met someone who understood her so well.

Talking therapies are the preferred route for addressing the increase in mental health problems, rather than administering anti-depressants and tranquillisers—the efficacy of which are unclear. A number of websites now offer Cognitive Behaviour Therapy (CBT) an effective means of dealing with forms of anxiety and depression. CBT is 'based on the assumption that prior learning is currently having maladaptive consequences' and the aim of CBT 'is to reduce distress or unwanted behaviour by undoing this learning or by providing new, more adaptive learning experiences' (NICE 2006).

CBT has been found to be an effective form of psychotherapy in randomised controlled trials for the treatment of anxiety and depression. Traditionally, CBT is delivered face-to-face by a trained therapist, but computers can also deliver it. Moreover, computer interventions have been shown to be at least as effective as those of human practitioners—and their time it is more available. Online systems are available twenty-four hours a day and can be delivered on a large scale, inexpensively.

Online psychiatry seems to be an ideal answer to the increase in mental-health problems, offering patients better access, reducing costs and improving efficacy. Today, if it comes to a choice between a highly personalised computer program, available day and night, with no waiting list or forty minutes with a busy human practitioner, I know which I prefer.

CONCLUSION AND FUTURE HEALTHCARE

Once a patient had to rely on a doctor's opinion, which was based on a collection of book knowledge, experience and rules-of-thumb. Nowadays, it seems odd that the value of doctors is founded on their machine-like qualities rather than on their human ones.

The fictional Dr Gregory House considers that talking to patients is what makes doctors miserable and prefers the quest for a diagnosis to a relationship with a patient. In part, he may have his way. Max Frisch once said: 'Technology [is] the knack of so arranging the world that we don't have to experience it.' But unfortunately for House, the future of medicine will be more about relationships with patients than inspirational diagnosis.

Computer-based treatment will become the norm. The resulting database of treatment and evidence will contain the combined experience of thousands of treatments. Doctors will take large risks if they deviate from practice, and can expect to be accountable for it.

Some doctors are still entranced by medicine as an art, rather than as a science. More structured medicine using computers, guidelines, and protocols will make medicine lose its soul, they fear. I think the contrary. In the future, touch, feel and understanding will be of far more value. Doctors will need the ability to listen to patients and to understand a patient's meaning, context and values and be motivated to act as the patient's advocate. Medical students of the future will need more empathy than memory.

SUMMARY

1. While the promise of sentient computers has not been met, the microchip is ubiquitous.
2. Medical knowledge is vast and stretches human memory and brainpower. Further, medical intuition, if it exists, is very expensive to procure.
3. When the clinical domain is well understood and can be diagnosed with confidence, machines are likely to be able to calculate better than humans. For example, chess is estimated to have more potential positions than there are atoms in the universe, and chess engines beat all but the very strongest players.
4. Expert Systems, is a field of Artificial Intelligence in which medical knowledge, such as evidence, guidelines and support, can be encoded and accessed by an inference engine thereby mimicking expert thinking. Examples that support human practitioners already exist.
5. Computerised Cognitive Behavioural Therapy in the treatment of mental illness has been shown to be at least as effective as the same intervention provided by a human practitioner—and it is more reliable and available.
6. Future health practitioners will be more highly valued for their human qualities rather than machine-like qualities of memory and cold inference. With the support of machines, and in adopting greater structure, Medicine will gain its soul, rather than lose it.

CHAPTER SIX
INFORMATION TECHNOLOGY
CAN SAVE THE NHS

Information is the fundamental currency of healthcare: from patient to clinician; from diagnostic test lab to clinician; and from clinical interventions to executive directors and the Board. You would think that such an information-dense industry would value the smooth flow of data. You would be wrong.

The NHS developed as a set of distinct entities and organisations, perhaps because its sheer scope made it difficult to manage in any other way, and, because, as we have seen, medical knowledge is so vast that it is impossible for one group to grasp it all. In the NHS information is centred on organizations, disciplines and even individual clinicians.

The NHS has been unsuccessful in creating a shared record to support patient care. And nowhere were the difficulties set in sharper relief than during the NHS National Programme for IT (NPfIT). The Programme's goal was to create a shared electronic health record. The tensions that erupted between doctors, clinicians, managers and suppliers were painfully public and were the single most important factor in the Programme failing to achieve its goal.

PERSISTENCE OF PAPER

In ancient Egypt gangs of priests guarded precious papyrus scrolls. In today's NHS departments of clerks chase and serve the paper record in a similar manner.

Of course, the paper record shares the same qualities as other bits of paper it: gets lost; becomes defaced; becomes illegible; gets mixed up with other bits; needs vast volumes of storage...need I go on? Alright then. Patient records also don't arrive at outpatient appointments leaving the doctor asking the patient: 'What did we do to you last time?' The old joke is that the record is often in the boot of a consultant's car, but more often it is in a pile on a medical secretary's desk. Hoarding of records is the norm—that way at least you know where it is, right? Even when the record arrives with the patient—admittedly most of the time—it is often so badly organised that the clinician cannot quickly find anything relevant. Yet the main information technology of the twenty-first century NHS remains paper.

Even where information is relatively good and accessible—say at GP practices, or in departments like Intensive Care where rows of machinery collect masses of data—the problem is in sharing it. There seems little point in having excellent data if it cannot be shared with other aspects of care. The health system is like a compound eye that has many views of the patient, but without an underlying nervous system and brain to bring them together. You are never a whole person to the NHS. You are a collection of specialties and a customer of one of the subunits—like a GP practice or an acute hospital—of course social care adds to complexity for some as yet another unit.

Can IT solve this problem? Not entirely. Expensive IT in a fractured organisation is unlikely to improve much. Nonetheless, IT is indifferent to physical location, caring little about organisations. This allows it to be a mainline that may anneal the NHS into an organisation that sees a patient rather than a collection of records.

NO SHARED RECORD

One billion Facebook users share intimate details of their lives: photographs, life events and interests online. And anyone watching their GP hunt and peck her way around a PC keyboard may think that the NHS shares a similar record of their care. They would be wrong.

Electronic records are rarely shared between organisations, other than records of transactions. While there are some enlightened exceptions, the whole set of records is rarely shared. This means care is rarely integrated and the patient is the glue that joins the fragments of information that have managed to pass between silos.

It would make sense to keep all that information about your health in one place, right? And to make it accessible to anyone that you choose as a health advocate? Rather like choosing with whom you share a record of your life on Facebook?

QUEST FOR EFFICIENCY

To meet demand in the post-credit-crunch world, the NHS is going to have to absorb increases in demand with the same level of funding. Effectively this means an increase in efficiency of about five percent a year. The NHS has already deployed its primary weapons of cutting staff, cutting services (by whatever euphemism), and consolidation where local politics allows.

The current panacea is consolidation and centralisation with the hope that economies of scale will help the NHS to survive. I doubt this will suffice. It may help the NHS to survive the next two to three years, but not the next ten. We shall see later that one of the main problems is healthcare's passion for large institutions, therefore all consolidation may do is to create a larger Titanic.

Nonetheless, efficiencies are possible. Many acute hospitals are trying to reduce unplanned care and increase planned. Sometimes these efforts are thwarted by a tendency of inexperienced staff in the A&E department to admit patients rather than take any risk. The greatest load on A&E departments is often patients with long-term conditions who are on their cycle between acute, primary, community and social care.

Often patients admitted on a Friday can occupy an expensive acute bed for a whole weekend unnecessarily, because there is no senior doctor to discharge them. It is obvious that preventing recourse to acute care and treating patients in, or close, to their homes is not only better for patients, it is also less expensive for the NHS and social care.

Overall, admission and escalation is the systemic problem of a fractured care service which will only worsen as the incidence of chronically-ill patients increases. Better IT could help to heal the fracture.

It is clear the NHS needs substantial changes to its working practices. But in the current context these can do little more than speed up a system at capacity. Further, the NHS is essentially a nine am to five pm service in a twenty-four hour world. This leaves expensive assets like operating theatres and imaging equipment under utilised.

All of this is a mismatch with the expectations of the digital generation who are used to service at their fingertips day and night. At an abstract level the NHS has three options: reduce demand; deal with demand more efficiently; and discharge patients quickly from expensive to less expensive care. A twenty-first century health system needs to address all three and, as we will see, effective use of IT can be a fundamental enabler of that.

ERRORS

The National Audit Office has suggested that about ten percent of patients receive inappropriate treatment. But no accurate measure of the number of patients who die as a direct result of their care exists. Estimates range from 7,000 to more than 20,000 a year. The National Patient Safety Agency encourages so-called adverse events to be recorded openly, but there is no way of knowing whether the information it collects is comprehensive.

One of the areas where IT can assist is in the prescription and administration of drugs. Pharmacists and junior doctors still have to decipher doctors' handwriting, and nurses attempt to keep track of whether the drugs prescribed have been administered using the usual selection of paper-based records.

Human error is inevitable. It is all too easy for incorrect drugs to be prescribed and for administration to be forgotten. It therefore follows that we should make it as difficult as possible for fallible humans to err. Computers can offer a range of customisable alerts on patient allergies, ensuring barcodes on drugs match a patient's prescription, and that patients are not given the wrong intravenous feed with potentially fatal results.

NEED FOR SCIENTIFIC MEDICINE

Robert M Pirsig in *Zen and the Art of Motorcycle Maintenance* said: 'The real purpose of the scientific method is to make sure nature hasn't misled you into thinking you know something you actually don't know.' When I first came to healthcare fresh from completing my MBA, I was high on ideas of quality management. I thought that anyone rational would see the advantage of recording, assessing and improving practice. I was in for a shock.

In leading my first electronic patient record programme in a London teaching hospital, I found doctors warmish at the prospect of having transactional information, like diagnostic test results and visit information, but distinctly cool at the prospect of recording outcome information.

To collect up-to-date, systematic reviews of all relevant randomised controlled trials of healthcare, the Cochrane Collaboration was founded in 1993—perhaps the real birth date of Evidence Based Medicine (EBM).

EBM should encourage the analysis of the relationship between process and outcome, much like quality management, but much clinical practice still seems to have no evidence base. No-one that I have approached, including staff of some established peer-review journals, has been able to estimate confidently the percentage of healthcare with sound scientific evidence supporting it. It could be anywhere from ten to eighty percent, depending on how you interpret the figures. This suggests that a large portion of conventional medical practitioners are relegated to the same league in which EBM zealots place homoeopathists or nutritionists.

I have also been unable to find any figures that suggest that the percentage of medical practice supported by sound evidence has increased. Indeed, some studies suggest a general reluctance among clinicians to adopt EBM. The reason is not clear and it is not in the scope of this book to seek it. I would simply say that having scientific medical practice seems like common sense to me.

To some extent the adoption of EBM suffers from the same difficulties as the rest of medicine: it is growing rapidly and it is impossible for human practitioners to keep up. Many complain they are swamped with information, and systematic reviews pile up in their offices with no prospect of ever being read, let alone integrated into practice.

Every clinician should have immediate access to best practice with the supporting evidence and have the skills to understand it and the resources to implement it. The reality is better treatments may exist, but not every clinician will know about them, or even seek them out.

In the storage and management of huge volumes of data, IT excels. Data that can be used to relate practice to outcome; data that can be easily updated to incorporate changes based on the best evidence; data that can be searched easily; data that are easily accessed.

An interesting analogy comes from a new version of the popular chess-playing engine Fritz. As well as being a formidable chess player, it allows chess positions to be entered, analysed and shared. Online you can identify other players who have already analysed the position, or who are in the process of doing so. It is easy to see a parallel between the development of the best moves from a given position to the development of best practice for a given condition.

Information is centred around organisations and practitioners rather than around you and me—the patients. Comprehensive, patient-centred, shared information would create huge quantities of rich data which could be analysed by ever-increasing computer processing power to detect patterns of behaviour, disease and treatment on an unprecedented scale. If chess players can do it, so can clinicians.

STRUCTURED MEDICINE

Making medicine more structured makes perfect sense to me, but then I am someone who has a standard list for everything: conferences, short business trips, house moves. I am also a believer in evidence, rationality and in reducing the scope for error by employing a comparable, reproducible method that can be easily modified as practice develops.

For some time it has been known that the treatment of most conditions follows standard pathways. Computers are very good at the management of pathways—think quest games—making it easy to note variances and assess how they may have affected outcomes. The grouping of patients

[handwritten annotations at top of page: "of it - Information / Genomics - epigenetics - WF - Patient ideome / Patient expectations - Dementia / co-morbidity"]

also has a good fit with genomics and might use a person's genome as a yardstick.

Now there is plenty of clinical criticism of this argument, especially when it comes to the management of complex co-morbidities, or the need for a judgment in the event of an unexpected set of symptoms. But I have already said that we are looking at partnership between man and machine. No-one is expecting machines to take over medicine (at least not yet) but they can help—and increasingly so. Also, as experience in working with structure and machines increases, so will our ability to make the best of them—including anticipating the presentation and treatment of co-morbidities.

However, rather like EBM, doctors have not rushed to adopt structure. Some refer to it as 'tick-box medicine' and regard it as a restriction on clinical freedom—whatever that might be. But for whom is clinical freedom such a great thing, for the patient or for the doctor? Until we have structured practice and comparable outcomes we will never be confident of the answer to this question.

CRADLE TO GRAVE

G K Chesterton suggested that every revolution is a restoration—the re-introduction of something that once guided people. The original goal of the NHS was to be a cradle-to-grave health service for the UK. But the lion's share of the £100 billion plus of NHS funding is spent on mending the unwell. And that spending is set to increase as we become overweight and more prone to chronic disease.

All of the issues we have touched on in this chapter can be addressed—at least in part—by something that has become part of our lives: IT. Its unique and ubiquitous nature offers a tool to address them all. Senses can be replicated, monitoring can be continuous, records can be shared—overall man and machine can forge a new model of healthcare.

SUMMARY

1. Though information is the basic currency of healthcare, IT has been marginalised. The overriding technology of the NHS is still paper, with all of its disadvantages.
2. The NHS has no single, shared, patient-centred record.
3. Though reorganisations are seeking to make the NHS more efficient by about five percent a year, they are unlikely to make all of the savings needed.
4. The NHS needs to reduce demand and deal with any demand more efficiently.
5. The NHS is essentially an analogue nine-to-five service in a digital twenty-four hour world.
6. Human error is still a major cause of adverse events and even death.
7. Evidence Based Medicine and the associated need for storage and regular updates are not easily managed by humans.
8. Information Technology (IT) systems are very good at managing structured information.
9. The majority of NHS funds are spent on mending the unwell. It is a sickness service rather than a health service.

CHAPTER SEVEN
DIGITISING MEDICINE: EVERYTHING, EVERYWHERE, ALWAYS

In your washing machine, attached to supermarket goods, in your pocket in your mobile phone: microprocessors are everywhere. What's more they continue to get faster and less expensive. Moore's Law originated around 1970. Essentially, it states that microprocessor speed, or computer processing power, will double every two years. It has proved remarkably accurate.

Around 2020 the price of a chip is expected to fall to about one penny, which is about the price of a piece of paper. At this stage, computing will disappear and become fully integrated into our lives—yes, even into healthcare. What's more, in these days of cloud computing, organisations do not even need to own the computers, calculating power can be leased. And we have a technology that can link all of those individual, cheap chips together.

WIRELESSNESS

As I walk down Oxford Street in London, I have to keep an eye open for those who walk in a half world of real and representation with their mobile phones. Changing music, checking the route, calling a companion. We live in a world where wireless connection is almost everywhere and it has integrated into our lives seamlessly.

Wireless frees us from physical location and connection and may free care from the constraints of walls and organisational boundaries. It also promotes connectivity allowing us to move from area to area while enjoying a continuous service, or by offering us a new service based on our activity and what we are carrying.

We are familiar with cell phones and Wi-Fi, but there is a range of wireless connectivity technologies already here or emerging that allows communication over long and short distances.

For long-range wireless, 3G wireless is now fairly standard around the world. 3G has become so inexpensive that Amazon bundles it into its *Kindle*, with payment combined into the book price. But 4G wireless technology, already available in main UK cities, promises bandwidth and speeds similar to those of our home broadband.

Wireless connectivity will soon connect every device and object, and by 2020 as many as fifty billion devices could be interconnected through the Internet. In a wireless world we will expect healthcare to be like other services: fast, informed, interconnected, coherent and always on.

Propelled by a wireless wave, IT is becoming pervasive and integrated, rather than narrow and standalone and so must healthcare, therefore practitioners must ride the wave or be swept aside.

WIRELESS CHIPS

It seems inevitable that ubiquitous chips would be combined with ubiquitous wireless access to create a device.

....o Frequency Identification (RFID) tags are essentially an antenna attached to a microprocessor that allows a chip to transmit data in response to a wireless request. Tags may be applied to people and to objects, allowing readers on door frames, wards and treatment areas to detect and record interactions.

Tags can be active or passive. Active tags have a battery with a life of several years, a range of tens of metres and a larger data capacity than passive tags. Passive tags have no battery and use reader emissions to power a brief response, usually just an ID number. They have a short range—about ten millimetres to five metres—and they can be small enough to implant under the skin.

In healthcare tags have five main applications: identification and verification; tracking; alerts and triggers; recording and managing interventions; and sensing.

We have already noted that drug and patient matching errors remain a problem. The National Patient Safety Agency (NPSA) estimates that treatment errors occur in about 850,000 of the annual eight million admissions to UK hospitals. The cost to the NHS in terms of extra bed days is about £2 billion a year. The NPSA also estimates that many treatment errors are caused by incorrect patient identification.

Tags on wristbands could be a means of automatically identifying patients as they move in the wireless matrix that our hospitals will become.

RFID tags are already used to track everything from barrels to babies on Tyneside and pallets and penguins in the Arctic. A combination of active and passive tags could allow staff, assets, patients, consumables—in fact, almost anything—to be tracked. It is also possible to imagine a world where everything would be labelled so we would only have to hover a reader over an object or person to be presented with information about it.

High-Street retailers who use passive RFID tags to manage supply chains are claiming cost reductions equal to about five percent of sales. In the same way, better management of stock on wards and in departments like theatres and A&E could potentially save the NHS millions of pounds.

Active tags on objects and people that enter a RFID reader's field can set off an alert or automatically initiate other events or processes. Tags on pharmaceuticals that uniquely identify a drug and its dose could be combined with electronic prescribing to prevent medication errors and reduce adverse drug interactions. Furthermore, the same tags could, for example, automatically trigger the ordering of a special diet or a series of blood tests appropriate to a drug regime. It is even possible for drugs to be tagged to allow compliance with a regime to be confirmed, making sure that a patient is actually taking their medication.

Manufacturers are already extending RFID by attaching sensors to tags, enabling changes in pressure, temperature, humidity and mechanical stress to be monitored. Such non-invasive monitoring could, for example, warn orthopaedic surgeons that a hip or knee prosthesis is about to fail, or reassure clinicians that reagents and drugs have been properly stored. An integrated temperature sensor can continuously monitor temperature-sensitive items in order to ensure that the contents are not compromised by temperature extremes.

Overall wireless technology and tagging can be used to create a comprehensive record of interventions using a combination of tagged objects and people.

Recently the quality, variety, accuracy and usability of electronic sensors have increased sharply while their cost has fallen. One of the most common sensors is the accelerometer—such as those in the *Wii* and *iPhone*—it can detect orientation; so, for example, photographs taken in portrait or landscape mode are imported the right way up.

Microsoft's *Kinect* senses motion and can be connected into game consoles. Game users can interact with devices like the *Xbox 360* without the need for physical contact with the device or a controller by using gestures and voice commands. *Kinect* also supports gesture, voice and face recognition allowing people to be simultaneously tracked, the number only being limited by the field of the camera.

Microsoft has released some elements of its *Kinect* device for development by third parties; for example, skeletal tracking that enables people to be tracked. Researchers have already applied *Kinect* in the diagnosis of a range of disorders in children; for example, autism, attention deficit disorder and obsessive compulsive disorder. Furthermore, surgeons are using the technology to manipulate diagnostic images during procedures.

Smartphones have become a vector for all sorts of ingenious applications that make use of sensors. Sensors are used in gaming; for example, in *Angry Birds*. Location can of course be determined using GPS (and less accurately by cell triangulation) and cameras are now a standard in even the cheapest phones.

The combination of sensors, sensors and microprocessors opens the way for all manner of healthcare applications. Tagged people and objects can be used to track interventions and create the ultimate medical record.

DATA INPUT

One of the biggest bugbears of current technology is user input. The need to use the awkward keyboard as the main device for input slows down many of us. We have already seen that greater use of wireless tagging could automate data input freeing the user to care rather than to type or tap.

One technology that has held promise for some time is speech recognition. My own experience of this is varied, I have purchased, and discontinued using, at least two versions of a well-known package. Even if error rates can be reduced to the order of five percent, that still means that one word in twenty will be incorrect. Furthermore, manufacturers face diminishing returns, where gaining marginal improvements in that error rate will be increasingly expensive and offer decreasing profit. Nonetheless, tags and speech-and-gesture recognition seem to be the way of future data input.

DATABASES

Databases have been around for so long that we tend to forget about them. *Facebook* is essentially a database with a friendly face created by its users. Recent years have seen advances in the way databases can be queried and about how golden insights about customer behaviour, perceptions and preferences can be extracted from a mountain of dross.

The collection of structured data by using, for example, clinical coding like SNOMED, when related to genomics has the potential to create knowledge on an unrivalled scale. Search technologies make it easy to extract information and to find patterns and interrelationships.

COMPUTERS BECOME SEXY

I have fed computers with stacks of punched cards; lost hours of work at three am owing to a dodgy memory pack for a *Sinclair ZX81*; watched the onslaught of the PC; and been swept along by the Internet revolution—but only recently have I seen computers go from geeky to sexy. IT has gone from wearing the T-shirt of a heavy metal band to wearing seven inch heels and a mini-skirt.

Perhaps it is down to the ubiquity of the mobile phone. Perhaps it is Apple computers—you only have to visit one of the company's temples on the high street to see what an attraction they are to young and old. I recently attended a presentation at the Apple Store on London's Regent Street entitled *Big Data and the Little Black Dress* from which it is clear that IT is now essential to the fashion industry. Not only in the use of social media to market goods, but also in the use of wireless tags to track stock in stores and to count the number of 'lifts' of an item from a shop floor hanger to determine its popularity.

Then maybe it's the appearance of tablet computers on *Holby City* and other healthcare soaps, because a similar wave has swept through healthcare. I now get clinicians asking me if they can use tablets to view data and discharge patients on wards.

Really, who cares why, because after pushing healthcare IT uphill for twenty years, it is refreshing to enjoy a downhill run.

ELECTRONIC PATIENT RECORD

Users of *Facebook*—where intimate thoughts, photographs, birthdays, phone numbers and email addresses are shared with friends around the globe—might think sharing their patient record—which after all is a similar combination of images, text, and figures—would be a cinch, right? Wrong.

Some may be expecting me to write a long section on this subject, particularly if I were to include the machinations of the NHS National Programme for IT (NPfIT) whose goal it was to create a cross-organisational patient record. They will be disappointed.

I don't because the concept of a single patient record shared across the NHS is easy to grasp—though far more difficult to implement. What's more, much academic angst has already gone into trying to define the patient record: is it time based, is it disease based, is it a narrative, is it based on episodes of care, or is it based on transactions?

Reading some of the academic output on this topic, I am amazed that clinicians are able to practise at all, because they seem to lack a definition for such a fundamental element of their work. Fortunately, lack of ability to define does not mean lack of ability to use, otherwise clinicians would never be able to make do with today's jumble of paper and disconnected digital.

Now, to be shareable, practitioners need to store records consistently in a compatible format. SNOMED CT (Systematised Nomenclature of Medicine Clinical Terms) is a computer processable system of recording medical terms encompassing diseases, symptoms, procedures, substances, and so on. Once encoded, clinical information can be organised and cross referenced. However, when combined with developments in genomics the result could create a sword to the Gordian knot, allowing healthcare to be structured, analysed and evidenced as never before.

The drawback of SNOMED CT is its comprehensiveness. For clinicians working in a specialty there are probably a limited number of terms to use—after a while clinicians can probably remember them. But in general medicine the number increases astronomically. To some extent this can be mitigated by encoders, and a natural language interface will help even more.

An electronic patient record could be likened to the database underlying *Facebook*. Associated with it would be transactional systems, such as a doctor being able to request, and receive, the result of, diagnostic tests. On the ward drugs could be prescribed in similar transactions and their administration recorded, checking drug interactions and incompatibilities. We have already seen that the incorrect identification of patients can be the cause of medical errors, and a recent study in the University of Birmingham NHS Trust suggested that about twenty percent of drug administrations on wards are missed.

The US Department of Veterans Affairs developed *VistA* (Veterans Health Information Systems and Technology

Architecture) an electronic patient record which is free to anyone. *VistA* concentrates on tracking patient care rather than transactions for billing—bodacious in the US profit-based healthcare system. The VA also claims to offer the best care anywhere and is similar to the NHS in being dependent on the efficient use of public money. It seems the creation of an electronic patient record system in a public sector organisation is neither impossible nor incompatible with good care.

PERSONAL HEALTH RECORD

GP Dr Amir Hannan took over the practice in Hyde in Manchester formerly owned by Britain's worst serial killer, Harold Shipman. Unlike Shipman, Dr Hannan has nothing to hide and intends to allow his patients to view their medical records over a secure internet connection in an effort to rebuild lost trust, demonstrate openness and show exemplary record keeping.

Other GPs are less keen to share. The Summary Care Record that was developed by NHS NPfIT and which comprises only a subset of the GP record is still only patchily implemented in England.

Now these records are about my health, maintained by doctors on computer systems—both of which are funded by my taxes. But is seems I do not own my own health record. I can't even see it without a special request. Note that without organisations, the subject of record sharing is reduced to one of my permission, since to IT the physical boundaries that define human domains are irrelevant. Therefore, the hullaballoo that surrounds information sharing in the NHS is just that.

The policy of the current UK coalition government is not only to allow patients to access their record, but also to allow them to control it. Given the apparent appetite of most GPs for these ideas, implementation of policy promises to be an interesting debacle. Nonetheless, personal control of records bypasses the organisational dynamics that characterise NHS care and releases constrictions to information flow.

The *Facebook* generation is used to managing access to its personal information. Therefore, rather like the privacy settings on my *Facebook* page, I should determine who has access to my record. Also, we have already seen that *Google* probably knows more about me than my GP anyway. So, is a personal health record such a radical concept?

PICTURE ARCHIVING AND COMMUNICATIONS

There are legions of health IT applications. I mention one more because it seems to represent an exemplar. The Picture Archive and Communication System (PACS), which was widely rolled out as part the NPfIT, allows the digitisation, storage and sharing of diagnostic images. It is a great success. PACS has demonstrated how digital information can be shared and form the basis of close co-operation between clinical disciplines regardless of location or care setting. Images may even be discussed with patients during a consultation. All healthcare IT should aspire to the condition of PACS.

Having the right technology and applications could make a profound difference to the delivery of care—and the main blockages are not technical, they are human.

SUMMARY

1. The price of computer chips continues to fall as their power increases. It will soon be possible to chip almost everything.
2. Wireless is also ubiquitous. Combine wireless with chip, and you could unobtrusively interconnect everything with everything else—staff and objects. Furthermore, combine wireless tags with increasingly sophisticated sensors, like Microsoft's *Kinect*, and you could interconnect everything in a sentient network.
3. Data input could be simplified as the combination of tagged people and objects creating the ultimate medical record, contactlessly.
4. Databases, where structured information is stored, are often forgotten, yet they are essential to the function of modern applications like *Facebook*. More sophisticated database technology can be used to extract nuggets of knowledge from a mountain of data dross.
5. Computers have become sexy and are no longer the sole domain of the male geek.
6. An Electronic Patient Record is an easy concept to understand, particularly for users of social media, where text and images can be easily shared. It has proved to be far more difficult to implement.
7. Structured information can be collected and coded using systems like SNOMED CT. This would allow easy analysis. Moreover when combined with advances in Genomics it could offer an unparalleled research tool

that allows clinical process and outcome to be related to genetic profile.

8. A shared patient record in public sector healthcare is entirely feasible, as the Veterans Health Association in the US has amply demonstrated.

9. Personal Health Records are also practicable to a generation that is used to maintaining and sharing its own record on social media. What's more, personal control would free the records from any organisational constraints that may prevent beneficial sharing.

10. Without a whimper, the NHS adopted digital diagnostic imaging with Picture Archiving and Communications Systems (PACS). Medical information is shared regardless of discipline and distance.

CHAPTER EIGHT

REMOTE CARE

In 1917 in Australia a local postmaster saved the life of Jimmy Darcy, a stockman, by operating on him under the Morse-Code guidance of Dr Holland, who was located 2,000 miles away. The postmaster used straps, whisky and a penknife and operated on the office counter. This story was told to support the case for the formation of the Aerial Medical Service, one of the forbears of the Royal Flying Doctor Service of Australia.

More recently, I consulted a GP over the telephone, and he prescribed antibiotics to treat a painful bout of sinusitis. Care has been delivered remotely for decades, so the idea is not new, yet it now represents a form that healthcare struggles to absorb.

WHAT IS TELEHEALTH AND WHO CARES?

Most people find it easy to grasp the idea of care over a telephone or by a video conference or a smartphone, but—rather like the electronic patient record—a lot of time and brainpower has been expended in trying to define it. Clinicians and academics have ignored Occam's Razor and sliced and diced telehealth into as many segments as twenty-first century medicine. Should we discriminate on the basis of time, specialty, patient location, patient's care setting, the equipment used, the responsiveness of the equipment used? Telehealth has been defined to death by academics and clinicians. It's a shame that its implementation did not attract the same level of enthusiasm.

Telemedicine, as defined by the WHO, is '...the practice of medical care using interactive audio visual and data communications. This includes the delivery of medical care, diagnosis, consultation and treatment, as well as health education and the transfer of medical data.' Telehealth apparently allows patients to be monitored by self-applied sensors. Readings can be taken at intervals, often daily. Teleconsultation replaces face-to-face contact between patients and their carers, clinicians or doctors. Training is often carried out using live teleconferencing. So we have telemedicine, telehealth, teleconsultation, not to mention teletrauma, telenursing and telepharmacy—bewildered yet?

One of my reviewers proposes three simple definitions, the other tele-whatnots being some variation of these:

Telemedicine: A clinician monitoring patients remotely.
Telehealth: A clinician supporting a patient to monitor their own condition.
Telecare: A clinician supporting daily living (usually social care).

As you will guess, I am not a tele-definition person, because I consider IT necessary to support all forms of healthcare, whoever provides it. The main thing for me is that it is used to deliver care as seamlessly as possible. Which organization or discipline takes responsibility for that delivery is a matter which I will address later.

Telehealth seems a good enough term to me. The main differences in these definitions are much the same as they would be in conventional medicine (or many commercial processes for that matter). Sometimes the task can be carried out without the clinician or patient being present, such as when reading diagnostic tests or when the tests are self-administered. Sometimes activity is simply recorded and if there is an anomaly it triggers an alarm. Sometimes the patient needs to be monitored in real time and interventions carried out interactively. Isn't all of this rather like the delivery of care now? So what is the big deal?

An obsession with definition and labelling in healthcare usually signposts an idea that is too scary or that no-one knows what to do with. Generally, IT is an enabling technology that should support all care. It is not an intervention or a specialism—and neither is telehealth.

SENSORS

One of the commonest applications of telehealth uses wireless pendants that connect wearers to their telephone systems. Other schemes use web cameras and sensors that detect the use or movement of domestic equipment or use videoconferencing, GPS and increasingly smartphones. Sensors are key to the success of telehealth. They alert to potential or real danger. For example, by noting if a person turns on their taps or opens and closes doors; by lighting a dark passageway; or by alerting patients when it is time to take medication.

The scope of telehealth is constrained by the degree that sensors can replicate our senses. Sight and hearing are well supported. Sensors also assess pressure, temperature and movement. Physiological signs like ECG traces are easily digitised. Remote molecular analysis of samples is also possible, which might to some extent replicate smell and taste.

Telehaptics uses sensors to transmit sensations from one location to another. The sensors detect tactile information and translate it to effectors that we can sense. It is also possible that brain activity or bodily sensations could be converted into signals, perhaps by using electrodes to stimulate the skin. If we combine wireless Telehealth with genomics then we may even create a sixth sense of prescience that allows us to see trouble ahead and avoid it.

It is no surprise that the development of devices that monitor blood pressure, heart rate, weight, blood glucose and haemoglobin levels are a growth area, because these have application to patients suffering from chronic conditions, who represent the majority of NHS activity.

Once again the real problem for the present is not the development of sensors, but how the readings, alarms and interactions from sensors are to be managed. So once again we arrive at the root problem: how are these technologies to be integrated by the human systems that they support? What structure do those systems have and what plans does the NHS (and social care) have to create them?

BENEFITS OF TELEHEALTH

Telehealth has some obvious advantages:
1. **Convenience for staff and patient.**
2. **Reducing the time and cost of travel.**

3. Speed of intervention, and even its avoidance.
4. Reduction in infection risk.
5. Ease of remote team working.
6. Reduction in the need for a fixed location.
7. Ease of monitoring, allowing care to be focused on exceptions.
8. Making best use of centralised and scarce expertise.

Frankly, the benefits of telehealth are blatant. Moreover, part of the problem with the many assessments that have been done is that they fail to account for the social cost of healthcare—so the time I take off work to attend appointments and the cost of travel are often not accounted for.

APPLICATIONS OF TELEHEALTH

We have already seen that telehealth has been applied for years without any of the fuss associated with the implementation of the various tele-definitions that we looked at. More recently the wider use of digital images such as PACS—one of the successes of the NHS NPfIT—has facilitated a form of telehealth. Now clinicians, no matter where they are located, can see the same diagnostic images and discuss them. It is commonplace for cancer specialists to use PACS combined with teleconferencing for case review. PACS slipped into practice without so much as a whimper. In social care remote applications are used to:

1. Anticipate problems using sensors and physiological indicators.
2. Monitor daily activity to ensure someone is active.
3. Offer assistance when an alarm sounds.

I know from family experience that wireless pendant type devices connected to telephones work. My mother, now in her eighties, wears one and when she fell and was unable to get up someone came to help her in minutes. In other circumstances she could have been stuck there until someone visited or heard her calls.

Other applications monitor daily activity. These include sensors to detect taps and fridge doors being opened. Sensors may also set off alerts and triggers when a particular set of physiological symptoms is detected, or when someone has fallen over, or to confirm someone has taken their medication or even remembered to drink some water.

Dementia is a disease of age, and more than 800,000 people in the UK suffer from it and the number is growing. The majority of us, as we age, will prefer to live independently as long as possible in our own homes and remote care has the potential to support that. Further, GPS and wireless tagging can improve care by detecting when someone wanders outside a safe zone, for example. Of course, we will also feel more secure knowing that there is someone watching over us, particularly important if we live alone.

WHOLE SYSTEMS DEMONSTRATOR PROGRAMME (WSDP)

If I were bitten by a snake in the Australian outback, I don't think I'd question the evidence for the effectiveness of remote care before I called the Flying Doctor. Yet, in the application of IT to healthcare much common sense is forgotten.

In 2008 the UK set up the largest randomised control trial of telehealth in the world. It aimed to gather evidence and to learn lessons that might inform a wider implementation. It involved 6,000 patients with long-term conditions and more than 230 GP practices. Patients included in the trial had one of three long-term conditions: diabetes, heart failure or COPD (Chronic Obstructive Pulmonary Disease). Half of the sample was used as a control, meaning about 3,000 actually participated. The trial found a reduction in:

1. Mortality rates by forty-five percent.
2. Emergency admissions by twenty percent.
3. A&E visits by fifteen percent.
4. Elective admissions by fourteen percent.
5. Bed days by fourteen percent.
6. Tariff costs by eight percent.

You might think that these were convincing (and not entirely surprising) outcomes, but they don't seem to have pleased everyone.

BARRIERS TO TELEHEALTH

There are more than 10,000 peer-reviewed papers on telehealth, yet no country in the world has implemented it on a wide scale. Everyone from the UK government to NHS staff have endorsed telehealth as the way of the future, but the scale of that enthusiasm is not yet matched by the scale of implementation. The main reasons for this are given as:

1. Problems of regulation.
2. Funding and value for money.

3. Cultural issues—which seems to have evolved into a catch-all phrase encompassing the consequences of any change and any resistance to it.
4. Lack of evidence—another catch-all phrase used to challenge anything uncomfortable and to fit with point three. Please recall a large chunk of Medicine has no evidence underpinning it, but that does not prevent it from being practised.

Telehealth cuts across the functions and interests of many powerful groups: GPs, acute hospitals, social care, care homes, even individual disciplines and specialties. For example, Pulse magazine, whose GP readership has a large financial stake in the management of long-term conditions, argued that telehealth was unlikely to be cost effective (8 March 2012). It also claimed a large telehealth project in Yorkshire was so under utilised that NHS managers had been forced to offer GPs a cash incentive to refer to it.

With results like those above, you have to ask where this antipathy comes from. Often the real tension in major health IT projects is not related to technology, patient outcomes or evidence, but to who gains and who loses among the affected power groups.

To address that we need to determine how we use this technology to best effect given the stakeholders. The WSDN did not pose that question. Had it tackled it, or at least created new merged pilot organisations and tried them out, its findings would certainly have been of far more value. While in some areas of the UK the relationship between primary and social care has been strengthened by the WDSN, in the majority of cases the turf wars continue.

Healthcare has been a reluctant adopter of any form of IT. To paraphrase (out of context) Prince Charles' assessment of the Sainsbury Wing of London's National Gallery, it has been added rather like a carbuncle on the face of a well-loved friend. Often the NHS constrains a potential carbuncle by a pilot, a tendency that led one the former heads of NHS IT to remark it had 'more pilots than British Airways'. Piloting and trialing seems to be a great way for healthcare to box and control anything that might challenge the status quo. The NHS has added IT to existing processes in an attempt to make them marginally more efficient. The result is to automate what the system already does, rather than to do something different and better.

Innovation often lies in the spaces between silos and so it is with telehealth. IT is no respecter of boundaries and tends to blur them or even eliminate them. Telehealth does not fit in existing silos. It requires a whole new organization—and maybe a whole new paradigm.

At his trial, the ancient Greek philosopher Socrates claimed that he should be rewarded for inflicting therapeutic pain upon his fellow Athenians. He encouraged Athenians to examine their principles and beliefs by relentless and clever questioning. He compared his effect on Athens to that of a gadfly on a sluggish horse. He liked to ask questions such as 'What is good?' or 'What is the pious, and what the impious?' Then, by adroit questioning, he would lead his victims to realise what they thought they 'knew' led to a contradiction.

I sense, in a similar way, healthcare is seeking to define, label and control what essentially does not fit with the established segmentation of care. Telehealth defies definition, labelling and pigeon holing. New applications of digital and wireless technology seem beyond definition in the same way as it would be difficult to use Ancient Greek to describe a smartphone. But simply because you cannot define something does not mean you cannot appreciate it or—in the case of telehealth—use it. Definitions and pilots have a place, but let's get on with implementing telehealth and learn from experience. Otherwise, like a hot bath, the more we contemplate it the colder it gets.

In no other healthcare domain are the issues associated with the integration of analogue and digital cast into sharper relief. Telehealth's application should only be limited by our imagination and ingenuity, yet it is constrained by indecision and obfuscation. It is not about double blind studies and winners and losers. It is about the efficient and effective delivery of care.

The Department of Health has begun a programme of telehealth, which it thinks will benefit people with long-term health or social-care needs. This is good news. In November 2012 the Minister of State for Health confirmed seven pathfinder schemes that will service 100,000 people in the next year or so. The overall goal is for three million people to benefit from telehealth by 2017.

The initiative is named *3millionlives* and will depend on a close working relationship between the NHS and telehealth vendors. In the longer term, the UK hopes to develop the skills and experience to make it a world leader in this field.

The initiative is welcome and—rather refreshingly after the more doctrinaire approach of NPfIT—makes it clear that it does not yet know all of the answers. However, this could be good or bad.

I have already said that the management of long-term conditions has a number of influential stakeholders—not surprising when it consumes about seventy percent of the NHS budget. Therefore, broader implementation is likely to require a great deal of management if it is not simply to be absorbed by business as usual.

Telehealth presents possibilities of cradle-to-grave care without any restriction on the location of carer and cared for. Think about it. That means the whole of the infrastructure, jobs and processes of the NHS could change completely if we embrace this technology. IT—and specifically telehealth—offers nothing short of a complete revision of the existing culture, mindset, structure and process of healthcare. We are talking revolution, not evolution.

SUMMARY

1. Remote care is not new.

2. Though an easy enough concept for most lay-people to understand, much time has been spent in trying to define remote care and thereby to squeeze it into clinical pigeon holes. Three definitions are (reluctantly) proposed: telemedicine, telehealth and telecare.

3. As in other areas, the development of sensors is key to the development of remote care. But the key question is how the output from the sensors managed; that is by whom and by what processes and organisation

4. Remote care has a lot of advantages, including removing dependency on physical location and making better use of scarce resources like medical expertise.

5. Telecare is used to allow the old and infirm to live independently confidently and safely.

6. The Whole System Demonstrator Programme (WSDP) was the world's largest randomised control trial of telehealth. The benefits from it were clear. Nonetheless, some groups are still sceptical of its value.

7. Though much has been written on telehealth and it has a great deal of support, this is not equalled by the scale of implementation. Many reasons are given for this: funding, regulation, lack of evidence. The most convincing argument is that telehealth cuts across the interests of many powerful groups. Indeed, the reason for the pursuit of a definition could be caused by this.

8. The Department of Health has a new programme called *3millionlives* that aims to promote wider implementation of telehealth.
9. Nonetheless, remote care means widespread change in NHS structure and process. It is not an evolution, it is a revolution.

CHAPTER NINE
REMOTE HEALTH MONITORING OR MOBILE FIREPOWER

George's road to hell began with a succession of illnesses. Then he endured agonising head pain for a week after discharge from hospital. After some persuasion from my mother—they are of a generation that prefers not to disturb doctors 'unnecessarily'—he had called the out-of-hours GP service, but the doctor attending said he could do little because he did not have George's medical record. So the agony continued. He was eventually diagnosed with a ruptured capillary in his skull.

A few weeks later, my mother, who is in her eighties, became concerned when she tried, unsuccessfully, to call George over several days. After alerting his family and even sending a friend to check his house, she thought she had done all she could. George was found by his daughter on his bathroom floor, paralysed and unable to speak having suffered a stroke four days earlier.

This ain't no technological breakdown—this is care in the twenty-first century.

MONITORING

Remote health monitoring is a reality. It is already possible to monitor basic indicators, like weight, blood pressure, pulse rate and blood sugar. But devices are becoming more sophisticated and cheaper and can be worn as armbands or, less obtrusively, in clothing.

Monitoring devices are already becoming available for smartphones. AliveCor's *iPhone ECG* system is a plastic phone case with two metal electrodes that can record heart rhythms when users clasp it between their hands or hold it against their chest. The real-time electrocardiograph data can be beamed to doctors or family members alerting them to any irregularities.

Vital signs like respiration and heart rate are useful indicators. A healthy heart rate has a high degree of variance, showing as a spikier trace than an unhealthy one. In addition, nocturnal breathing disorder is often a co-morbidity in asthma, COPD, hypertension and heart disease. Close monitoring of such signs could assist sufferers to manage their conditions and carers to pre-empt crises.

French company, Withings, has developed a blood-pressure monitor that works with an *iPhone* app. Users apply the cuff and readings are stored on the device.

Furthermore, it may be possible to diagnose the onset of mental illness from a person's speech. A depressed person speaks more slowly and software might spot that more accurately than a family member or a clinician. Also perhaps changes in a person's gait detected by motion sensors might indicate the onset of illnesses like Parkinson's disease.

And it doesn't stop with passive recording. Those of us who believe we are best placed to manage our own health can access apps such as NHS Direct. Based on the same algorithms used in the NHS Direct telephone service, it offers symptom checks for an array of common complaints such as rashes, burns, diarrhoea, and abdominal pain. It even has the facility for a nurse advisor to call you back.

HANDHELD DEVICES AND DOCTORS

The stethoscope is the tag of the junior doctor. It provides him with information, about heart and lung conditions. Yet a smartphone application *iStethoscope Pro* offers a twenty-first century alternative. With it you see and hear heartbeats and can represent them as waveforms. It also comes with a handy library of abnormal and reference forms.

Junior doctors have traditionally carried dog-eared reference books in the pockets of their white coats. Now they can refer that information, and much more, on a more convenient device. Moreover, digital information is random access and not sequential like a book. So a doctor can find the right section without turning down a page or relying on the book to fall open at a well-thumbed section. It is also easy to update reference material wirelessly with little effort.

British Medical Journal has produced a series of smartphone applications that give best practice in a number of disciplines. *Best Practice at a Glance* is a clinical assessment tool with more than 10,000 diagnoses and 3,000 diagnostic tests that are peer-reviewed. Users can access more than 4,000 full text diagnostic and treatment guidelines from international organisations and enjoy full access to the internationally renowned evidence database *Clinical Evidence*—and the integrated drugs database has 6,000 drug monographs. The application can also be tailored with local guidelines, patient information leaflets and links to other information.

The volume of medical information is growing, as are the applications which can draw upon it. This will lead to swifter diagnosis, treatment and monitoring wherever the patient and doctor happen to be.

MOBILE FIREPOWER

More than half of the world owns a mobile phone. Tens of millions of people in the poorest nations have already abandoned landlines. Further, about two thirds of all mobile phones now purchased in the UK are smartphones. And, I guess like me, people rapidly become addicted to them and they become an indispensable companion.

My smartphone wakes me in the morning, and I check my emails at breakfast (quicker than firing up the laptop). I check the weather; check the service on the London Underground; locate a customer's office using GPS; read a chapter of a book on the London Underground journey; check my notes online before the meeting; photograph an article in a free newspaper to read later; do the weekly shopping at the supermarket.

My smartphone has more calculating power than NASA deployed when it landed men on the moon in 1969. More worryingly, it probably has more calculating power than is at the disposal of my GP when I consult her. The cornucopia of the worldwide web is a couple of taps away—not to mention the rest of the apps I may have installed.

I can install applications that record my general health: weight, blood pressure, how physically active I have been. It is quite clear that I have the means to maintain a personal health record far more comprehensive than the NHS. Give me a secure website to store it on, and I can share my record with whom I like.

Universal use of mobile devices will be with us in the next decade, linked to telecommunications, data networks and satellites. Again the potential is only limited by our imagination and by our ability to prevent social exclusion caused by poor usability and affordability.

REMOTE CARE IN AFRICA

Necessity is the mother of invention they say. And lack of cash, shortage of resources and vast distances have generated the necessity for cheap and simple healthcare solutions in Africa. It is the fastest-growing mobile phone market in the world with an estimated 735 million users on the continent.

Even the poorest have access to a pay-as-you-go phone. Perhaps dodgy and expensive landline connections are the reason for the high use. But what is certain is that there are more mobile phones than doctors in Africa and most people are likely to have access to the former rather than the latter. Kenya, for example, has one doctor for every 10,000 people.

I am writing this on the twentieth anniversary of the sending of the first SMS message. One of the lowest tech areas of mobile telecommunications has become the most popular. Originally developed as a way for engineers to exchange short messages, it is estimated that now more than six trillion SMS messages are sent each year.

The Praekelt Foundation has exploited the penetration of mobile phones in Africa. *TxtAlert*, for example, sends automated SMS to patients with chronic diseases reminding then to take medication or perform other tasks. *Please Call Me* allows patients, even if they don't have phone credits, to ping their doctor who then calls them back.

Health eVillages was launched by the Robert F Kennedy Center and Physicians Interactive. It equips doctors with refurbished phones loaded with diagnostic tools like drug guides, medical alerts and summaries of journals and references. SMS messages can also spread alerts on the spread of disease. The programme has already been piloted in Haiti, Kenya, Uganda and the Greater Gulf Coast. The idea is to reach areas underserved by medical care.

The mHealth Alliance includes some of the largest organisations in the world. One of its projects includes an SMS counterfeit medication checker developed by Hewlett Packard—it is estimated that about twenty percent of drugs are counterfeit.

Medic Mobile supports home-based care, even if a doctor cannot visit. A pilot programme in Malawi is estimated to have saved carers about 1,200 hours of follow ups as well as large transportation costs. More than 100 patients received treatment for Tuberculosis when their symptoms were reported by text message.

Some of the poorest countries in the world, using basic technologies, are making better use of telehealth than their richer Western counterparts. Furthermore, in the future, wireless applications will help even more, allowing care to both centralise and devolve. Specialists can be centralised in monitoring and diagnostic centres—which will be invaluable to developing nations, where distances are often large and healthcare resources small.

I pause from typing this on my smartphone and look around the carriage on the London Underground. Half of the passengers are prodding and flicking mobile phones. A middle-aged couple share a copy of the *Times* or *Guardian* on a tablet computer. From devices we carry every day, we could monitor our health continuously. We *could* even record the whole of our lives and never forget an event again. Quite a medical record. Further, the wireless wave makes online services as immediate and continuous as the real world. We will expect healthcare to share those qualities.

It's too late for my mother's friend George, who died in hospital after suffering locked-in syndrome for a few months. Perhaps we will eventually be galvanised to action by stories like his and realise that while healthcare in the twentieth century was analogue, centralised, fractured, episodic and founded on disease management, in the twenty first it should be digital, devolved, continuous, integrated and founded on prophylaxis.

SUMMARY

1. Remote-health monitoring is already a reality. Sensors on mobile devices like mobile phones and smartphones can already monitor basic indicators, like blood pressure and heart and respiration rate, but they will become more sophisticated.
2. Genomics may also allow propensity to certain diseases to be predicted, allowing more focused monitoring with a certain degree of 'prescience'.
3. Smartphones and other handheld devices are powerful computers that facilitate access to online storage, resources and applications.
4. In Africa mobile phones are widely used as a means of tackling great distances with small healthcare resources. The humble SMS message has been used effectively to provide advice and reminders. Mobile phones are used as storage devices by doctors for carrying information on medication and best practice.

CHAPTER TEN

ROBOTS WILL LOOK AFTER US

After seeing Robbie in *Forbidden Planet* at the Saturday-morning pictures, my attempts to make a robot from shoe boxes, torch bulbs and a couple of dud batteries ended in failure. I have loved robots since I was a child, so you would expect me to say something like: doctors, nurses and carers look out for your jobs, the future of healthcare is here and it isn't human.

WHAT ARE ROBOTS?

Robots are a combination of software and mechanical parts. They are easily trained and have a long working life. Some can even replicate themselves. In essence, they are a moving array of sensors which allow them to see, gesture, navigate and communicate. Compared with humans, robots are quicker to train, cheaper to maintain, easier to refuel and repair and less prone to be bored by repetitive tasks—and you can get spare parts for them easily.

JAPAN AS AN AGEING SOCIETY

Japan faces a triple-demographic whammy. First, it has the most rapidly ageing population in the world with about twenty-five percent of the population being over the age of sixty five. Second, it has a falling birth rate. Third, the Japanese government keeps immigration extremely low.

Fortunately, Japan's human problems may be offset by its leading expertise with machinery. It has more than forty percent of the world's industrial robots and is applying that knowledge to healthcare.

EXAMPLES OF THEIR USE

Robots could help in the care of the elderly and chronically ill in four main ways:

1. **Addressing cognitive decline; for example, reminding patients to drink, take medicine or of an appointment.**
2. **Enabling patients and caregivers to interact remotely, thereby reducing the frequency of personal visits.**
3. **By collecting data and monitoring patients, emergencies, such as heart failure and high blood sugar levels, could be avoided.**
4. **Assisting people with domestic tasks, for example when people are feeling pushed towards giving up independent living because of arthritis.**

Toyota Motor Corporation has manufactured robots with the aim of supporting independent living. It has applied high-speed, high-precision motors to develop bipedal robots that operate using key-sensor technology.

Robots do the grunt work and act as support. One is designed to support the independent walking of people who have been injured or paralysed. When mounted onto the affected leg, it helps to promote natural walking. A similar design helps patients to learn to walk again. Another, a balance-training robot, is designed to help to retrain patients with impaired balance so they can move independently. Other designs help carers to move patients and heavy loads.

ASIMO

Honda's **ASIMO** *(Advanced Step in Innovative MObility)* is one of the most advanced bipedal robots in the world. Standing at 1.3 metres tall *ASIMO* can walk, run, run backwards, hop and jump. New developments in sensors also allow it to walk on uneven ground.

ASIMO is being developed to help people. It has been created as a new form of mobility. In the long term, it should allow you to execute a task without having to move yourself. It is also improving its ability to work harmoniously with humans—now, it can walk while holding a person's hand and carry objects using a trolley or cart.

As in other areas of remote care, sensors are the key to the development of robots. *ASIMO* uses visual, ultrasonic and floor sensors to recognise its environment. Moving with the aid of an eye camera and using wrist kinaesthetic sensors, it gives and takes objects. It has a fingered hand with sensors embedded in each finger, which allows them to move independently. The visual and hand sensors allow it to recognise objects and to perform tasks such as picking up a glass bottle and twisting off the cap, or holding a paper cup without crushing it. Of course, with a functional hand, it is now also capable of sign language.

Recently Honda has concentrated on developing *ASIMO* from an 'automatic machine' to an 'autonomous machine' with the decision-making capability to determine its behaviour according to its surroundings. For instance, it can predict the path of a person and avoid a collision.

ROBOT COMPANIONS

Some of Japan's aged are comforted by *Primo Puel*, an interactive doll that talks, giggles and even asks for a cuddle maybe helping to alleviate the loneliness of old age. But there is more to such robots than superficial cuteness. They monitor the aged, building up a pattern of their daily lives and watching for variations. If they spot something unusual, they alert relatives or carers to a possible problem.

Mitsubishi produces a one-metre-tall, smooth-talking amanuensis *Wakamaru*. It can live with human beings and can speak while looking at a person's face, shake hands with the person, and carry on natural conversation. It is powered by rechargeable batteries and moves around on wheels.

Available in male or female editions, it recognises up to ten faces and understands 10,000 words. *Wakamaru* can watch owners' houses while they are away (presumably with no chance of it throwing sneaky parties with its friends) and can also monitor the sick. It gives timely reminders to take medication and can alert carers if it thinks something is amiss.

REMOTE PRESENCE

I first came face-to-lens with a remote presence robot at St Mary's Hospital, Paddington, London where Professor Lord

---

Darzi's unit was exploring the integration of robotics into medicine and surgery.

The robot was operated over a secure broadband controlled from a console using a joystick. Patients could converse with a real doctor by a screen mounted on the robot's mobile base that mimicked the normal head movements of a human during conversation. The robot could also transmit heart and breath sounds and allow a remote doctor to view a patient and his charts. It also has applications in teaching and collaborative work.

SURGICAL ROBOTS

At the time I was meeting the remote presence robot, surgeons at St Mary's Hospital routinely operated with the *da Vinci* robot produced by Intuitive Surgical Inc. performing urological, cardiac and gastrointestinal procedures. Robots like the *da Vinci* can be seen as continuation of the general development in surgery from open to minimally invasive.

The *da Vinci* system has three main components: a viewing and control console (master) and a surgical arm unit (slave) and a laparoscopic stack. Using the robot, surgeons achieve unprecedented control and precision. The robot's endo-wrist restores freedom of movement in laparoscopic surgery almost to the extent of a human wrist. In addition, a surgeon's hand tremor, which is magnified by the lever-effect of the long, laparoscopic instruments, is eliminated and visibility improved by the stereoscopic view offered by the robot's two lenses.

Surgical robots are not programmable and do not work independently. They need human control or voice activation. However, they do make a surgeon's job less tiring, especially when such procedures may last for three hours or more. My own view is that it will not be long before such robots are able to act more independently. Advanced robots will also be able to perform microscopic operations on blood vessels, nerves and tissues.

INTELLIGENT ROBOTS

Artificial Intelligence has not lived up to early expectations. Most researchers are still clueless about the path to machine intelligence, short of the hope offered by increasing processing power. Even if robots could act autonomously, they may face another difficulty.

The 'uncanny valley' hypothesis suggests that when robots replicate our actions too closely they may lead to revulsion. The hypothesis was coined by Professor Masahimo Mori. He postulates that as a robot becomes more and more human, our response to it becomes more and more positive until a point is reached where this is replaced by revulsion. After this inflection point, human emotional responses become positive again. This undulation is referred to as uncanny valley.

Well, alright, though these developments are exciting, robots are still some way from the walking, talking, thinking machines of the movies. So, carers do not have to collect their P45s yet. Though some robots can walk, they still need to talk, think and be accepted if they are ever to challenge humans as carers.

The technology for robots that perform repetitive tasks based on fixed rules is mature and is widely used in manufacturing. The next generation of robots would include those that make decisions based on artificial intelligence; those that are capable of processing, analysing, and synthesising speech; and androids capable of interacting with patients and staff. Smaller processors, faster processing speeds and advances in machine learning techniques are the key drivers of the next generation of robots.

SOCIAL, LEGAL AND MORAL CONSEQUENCES

In one of my favourite books, *I, Robot*, Isaac Asimov conceived of machines with morals. His robots like nothing better than to sit and analyse the ethical implications of their actions. Could robots achieve this level of moral sophistication? Or would we constantly be in fear of them? And if robots could achieve this level of contemplation, would they be companions or slaves? Westerners have a negative preconception of robots, perhaps because of the way Hollywood has portrayed them. Interestingly, to most Japanese people robots are friendly and benign.

Even if robots succeed in improving their poor image in the West, their widespread deployment in healthcare would have many legal and moral consequences. For example, who would be responsible if they went wrong? The manufacturer or the NHS? Perhaps the robot would be like any other tool and the doctor or hospital would be responsible for its use.

$\sim$

BARRIERS TO ADOPTION

While robots are meant to help staff, it is inevitable that some jobs may be redundant. Plans to introduce robots into a hospital would cause uneasiness among staff and are likely to meet with objections and fear of job losses.

Moreover, I think most people (in the UK at least) would be uncomfortable interacting with robots. This may be especially true for patients, who already feel more vulnerable due to their health conditions. So, as attractive as Robbie seemed to me when I was a child, I think the wide-scale deployment of robots in healthcare is some way off.

SUMMARY

1. Robots are a moving array of sensors, software and mechanical parts.
2. They can be used to remind and monitor patients and to do some of the grunt work.
3. Japan's demographics and immigration policy mean it has one of the fastest ageing populations in the world. It is applying its knowledge of robotics to assist the aged.
4. Honda's *ASIMO* is one of the most advanced bipedal robots. It has hands with functioning fingers. It can also work in harmony with humans.
5. Remote presence robots can be manoeuvered from a distance and also support remote consultation. They could allow scarce expertise to be centralised and applied more widely.
6. Surgical robots can assist doctors by giving clearer views of the operating site and reducing the shake of laparoscopic instruments. In some centres, they are already used regularly.
7. In the West, robots have a negative image, and if they resemble humans too closely they can create revulsion in an effect named 'uncanny valley'.
8. Aside from as surgical assistants, it seems unlikely robots will be deployed in the NHS in the near future.

CHAPTER ELEVEN

IT AS A DISRUPTOR

In his book, *The Innovator's Prescription*, Clayton Christensen says healthcare is mired in two delivery models: the large general hospital and the local doctor's clinic. They have absorbed and withstood all of the innovations that have been thrown at them.

Christenson says that in the first decades of the twentieth century medical practice was an intuitive art, not a science—meaning that the ability to deliver care was embedded in the care-givers, not in rules, processes, and equipment. Large institutions developed around the care-givers and grew into complex knots of costs and processes. With too many care models under one roof, and complex organisations, it is difficult to measure the effectiveness of individual treatments. It is also difficult to measure the effect of change, because the untying of the relevant costs of a single process is impossible.

Though there have been innovations in day-case procedures and in the creation of centres of expertise, in the main the NHS has not strayed far from the comfort zone of the large institution. It is sometimes argued this is in the patients' interest, but is it? Industry tends to separate the specialist and costly from the reproducible and economical. Medicine needs to consider a similar approach. This is sometimes scathingly labelled 'cherry picking' by NHS clinicians, particularly if less complex cases are referred to independent or private-sector centres. It is not. It is simply making better use of expertise, resources and public money—and offering a better service to customers.

Governments and the Department of Health seem powerless to address this frozen duality, and almost any attempt to reorganise is met by resistance from the NHS and its customers—who are also inured of large institutions. Without someone willing to reduce the complexity, the institutional players are left defending their turf leaving little opportunity for innovation. If leaders lack the determination, power and resource to reconfigure the NHS, healthcare will remain locked in complex institutions that include at least two different models of care: specialist and commoditised.

In workshops I have led, many ideas about innovation amount to trying to make the existing system more efficient or about reconnecting care silos. The latter is a fertile idea. In general, much innovation can be found in the spaces between silos. The new GP-led Care Commissioning Groups (CCG), for example, are a further attempt to fix care co-ordination across organisational and cultural boundaries.

PROMOTING INNOVATION

Examples of the disruptive effect of technology are legion. Digital print processing disrupted traditional print media, who have in turn been disrupted by the new model of online and electronic publication. Traditional wire-based telecommunications were disrupted by wireless, which in turn is being disrupted by digital telephony services, like those offered by Skype. And the personal computer killed off mini- and mainframe computers and is itself under threat from smartphone and tablet devices.

Christensen also suggests that disruptive business models are created by new entrants to an industry, not by established institutions. Established institutions can often develop a disruptive technology, but rarely do they combine it with a disruptive operational model. Therefore, we need to take care that innovations and disruptive technologies are not blocked by institutional resistance and ingestion. The interests of society sometimes do not coincide with the interests of stakeholders in leading institutions. Recall that in Medicine we have an institution that rejected anaesthetics, asepsis, outpatients and minimally invasive surgery—all of which are now established practice.

Nor is it a convincing argument that lack of evidence prevents progress. As we have already seen, an undefined chunk of conventional medicine lacks sound underpinning other than someone's opinion. So, there is already a precedent for clinical practice based on the application of common sense and experience.

In addition, I do not think innovation is promoted by normalising approaches such as quality management. Current performance indicators seem to concentrate on process (waiting times, physiological measurements such as blood pressure and weight) and subjective patient experience rather than what I would term outcome.

What I want from an NHS intervention is for my lot to improve. I would be content to wait a bit longer, have a bit less personal contact, deal with staff who are more efficient than empathic, and so on, if I could be assured that at the end of it all, I was better off. Quality management does not promote radical innovation and is a means of measuring, comparing and controlling the efficiency of pre-existing models.

NEW TECHNOLOGY AND OLD THINKING

Often when a disruptive technology appears established practice disparages and rejects it. Because it tends to simplify complicated problems, existing experts feel it cannot possibly address the complex problems that they have been trained to address. Predictably then, the reaction of NHS experts to IT has been mixed.

I worked on an assignment at a hospital in Brighton a few years ago. It is located on the site of a former workhouse that opened in 1867, where the destitute would tramp to face a harsh regime. In that peculiar Victorian way, a benefactor presented the workhouse with a clock, which I could hear clanking above the office where I worked.

I often think of the NHS as a clockwork mechanism to which we have being adding digital parts. So, IT, a potentially disruptive technology, has been used to sustain an obsolescent mechanism. Powerful NHS groups have also inhibited change—probably unintentionally—and have helped to encase IT.

One of the characteristics of IT is its mutability. Those using *Facebook* note how quickly the look and feel of their page adapts to their preferences to create a more personalised service. The NHS still has its roots in the institutions and production methods of the twentieth century rather than the adaptable networks that characterise the twenty first.

IT is also capable of recording and storing vast numbers of data, not only for personalisation, but also as a means of tracking the efficacy of care. Medical knowledge is a journey, not a destination. Continual reflection, learning and revision should be part of that journey. Regrettably, that is not always the case. Sometimes there is little best practice, just good practitioners. Use of IT allows clinicians to share expertise easily. Imagine healthcare where better processes can be distributed in the background like the updates to the operating system on your PC or Mac.

IT is also scalable. The reliability of Moore's Law demonstrates how processes can be standardised, improved and manufactured at a lower cost—something that Silicon Valley has thrived on. In a similar way, IT will be able to encapsulate knowledge and expertise into a standardised form. When processes are standardised, they are easily updated and can be passed from expensive, highly-trained experts to less-costly technicians. The move from a paper-obsessed organisation to one based on electronic information will reduce costs, mistakes and variability at the very least.

INTERSECTIONS AND BOUNDARIES

Interesting possibilities often lie at the intersection of concepts, silos, organisations and disciplines. For example, Steve Jobs had a lifelong interest in the intersection of art and science, which led to the development of the Apple computer and ultimately the rise of the world's most valuable company.

When IT has been added to healthcare it has been done without any thought of how the NHS could work better. The goal of the NHS National Programme for IT was to create a cross-organisational patient record—perfect sense you might have thought—but the programme lacked an organisational vision. Benefits from technology arise from the human changes they underpin: computers buzz and humans do.

IT tends to merge and conflate structures. Experience shows the most squeezed are non-specialist middle managers and administrative staff. In addition, it is no respecter of physical boundaries and allows teams to form and function without walls, fixed locations and boundaries. These days the boundaries of primary, secondary and social care look increasingly like the coastlines of some prehistoric geography.

Traditional media such as newspapers, radio, and television still resemble a typical visit to a doctor's office—the information tends to flow in one direction only. Early healthcare websites were the same, acting primarily as information repositories meant for passive absorption by their users. However, social networking websites and 'Web 2.0' services have taken the Internet beyond its first incarnation to become a more interactive and user-created medium—another boundary crossed.

MODELS OF INNOVATION

The problems facing the healthcare industry aren't unique. At first the products and services of nearly every industry are complicated and expensive. Once only the wealthy had access to telephones, photography, air travel and cars.

A move to more economical care depends upon accurate diagnosis, precise treatment and new operational models.

Once a problem can be easily identified or, in the case of medicine diagnosed, the way is open and, codification, scalability and easy transferability are all qualities of increased use of IT.

The transfer from medical specialist to generalist has a good pedigree. For example, the administration of antibiotics was codified into a solution that could be administered by nurses. Hip replacements have been codified by standardisation of implants, tools and templates, moving them into the realm of the general surgeon.

Both type 2 and type 1 diabetes result in elevated levels of blood glucose, which puts sufferers at a higher risk of heart disease, kidney failure, blindness and other complications. The care of patients with type 1 diabetes has moved from specialist to patient. The care of type 2 diabetes, on the other hand, remains with the specialist. The diagnosis of the disease is the key to subsequent care and cost.

Diseases whose cause used to be uncertain, like cervical cancer and stomach ulcers, have now been shown to be infectious diseases that can be routinely treated by antibiotics or by vaccination. Some diseases can now be diagnosed using accurate genetic testing; for example HER2-positive breast cancer will increasingly move out of the hands of oncologists and into the realm of generalists. The care of HIV positive people has also been rapidly codified and moved to the generalist.

Moreover, a move to the commoditisation of Medicine opens the way for some care to be relocated out of large hospitals and into smaller, more controllable, and more economical institutions—thereby reducing cost and making outcomes more consistent. The key is in accurate diagnosis, and we have already seen sophisticated scanning equipment is smaller and less expensive, and, when used in local clinics, could reduce the need for patients to be diagnosed in large, expensive institutions.

Christensen suggests that diseases sit on a notional axis with intuitive, specialist medicine at one end and precise, general medicine at the other. As a disease is understood, can be easily diagnosed and then confidently associated with a regime of treatment, it moves closer to the precise, general end. This suggests at least two care models: solving imprecise, unstructured problems and solving precise, structured problems.

EXPERT SOLUTIONS

Imprecise, unstructured problems are in the realm of what Christensen calls 'Solution Shops'. The human body has a limited number of symptoms. So a patient presenting with stomach ache could have indigestion, gastro enteritis, constipation, stomach ulcer, and cholecystitis. The challenge is to draw the correct diagnosis from a few, often overlapping, symptoms.

Solving problems like this can be costly and take a large amount of resource. Rather like in an episode of *House*, doctors assess the symptoms and the results of various diagnostic tests and seek a feasible hypothesis, which they then test by applying the most feasible treatment. If that doesn't work, they collect more information, reformulate the hypothesis and try again.

Because the diagnostic process and the outcome are uncertain so is the cost. Solution Shops usually charge a variable fee, based on time and materials. The fee is usually high and in proportion to the value added.

OFF-THE-SHELF SOLUTIONS

When a problem can be easily identified and married with a solution, it can be addressed by a different model of care based on standardisation.

Examples could be routine joint replacement or the treatment of cataracts. At the outset, such procedures could only be carried out by experts; for example, Sir John Charnley invented the hip replacement and for a while was the only expert who could perform such an innovative procedure. Nowadays, prosthesis manufacturers standardise hip replacement into kits—instruments, templates and ranges of implants—to make the process more reproducible and to require a less rarified level of expertise and experience. Moreover, organisations using such models improve through practise, improving outcomes and making them more predictable. It also means that costs are more predictable and therefore adequate provision can be made for any outliers.

NETWORKS OF CARE

People with some ailments, like alcoholism and diabetes, join support groups, but the Web and the development of social media have made these groups easier to find and more convenient. Interactive networks, founded on a culture of openness, allow sufferers to share experiences and to measure the progress of their disease as never before.

One obvious application of a network is in the management of long-term conditions. When you are a member of a network, you have the security of a system that is always there, and the comfort of knowing you are sharing experiences with people who have similar conditions. But we have already seen that such networks exist already for diabetics and sufferers from coeliac disease.

Christensen's ideas do not fit with the fragmented way in which care has been delivered in the UK. IT can underpin this disruption if the NHS, as monopoly provider, can be prevented from simply absorbing it into existing delivery models in a way that simply adds cost. But that is easier said than done.

SUMMARY

1. Healthcare is mired in two delivery models: the local clinic and the large hospital. These have absorbed or withstood all of the innovations that have been thrown at them.
2. The models developed when medicine was an intuitive art centred on highly-trained experts.
3. Large institutions become cost centres and knots of allocated costs, which makes it difficult to determine which processes, treatments and interventions are economical and effective.
4. If diagnosis and treatment can be tightly linked and standardised, then they can be reproduced at scale in a similar way to that in which the microchip has increased in power but reduced in cost.
5. IT is a disruptive technology that offers scalability, mutability and data generation. It can also work across organisations and silos producing possibilities for innovation.
6. Once diagnosis and treatment can be reliably yoked, treatment can be standardised and then carried out in specialised centres.
7. Centres of experts are needed when diagnosis and treatment are uncertain. The diagnostic processes are costly and must be carried out by highly-trained experts.
8. Long-term diseases and other conditions can be supported by networks of care, with users sharing experiences and enjoying specialist facilities and support.
9. IT is disruptive technology only if it is not absorbed into existing models.

CHAPTER TWELVE

UNEASY PAST OF THE NHS AND IT

'And it ought to be remembered that there is nothing more difficult to take in hand, more perilous to conduct, or more uncertain in its success, than to take the lead in the introduction of a new order of things. Because the innovator has for enemies all those who have done well under the old conditions, and lukewarm defenders in those who may do well under the new.'
—Niccolo Machiavelli, *Il Principe.*

I have described a range of innovations and applications using IT, some new models, and even a new paradigm for healthcare. Therefore, by this stage you may be expecting me to conclude by joining the two into a call to action. Not yet. Many agree the NHS needs reform, but few agree on how to go about it. So let's look at some problems first.

He who controls the information runs the show. The organisational dynamics associated with the implementation of extensive IT systems have fascinated me for twenty-five years. Any major programme, IT or otherwise, that fails to allow for organisational politics is cruising to failure. Nowhere was this better demonstrated than in the NHS National Programme for IT (NPfIT).

~

WHAT WAS THE GOAL OF NPFIT?

Billed as the world's largest IT project, the UK's £20 billion (or whatever estimate you prefer) NPfIT tried to change the system. It aimed to connect more than 100,000 doctors and 400,000 nurses and other healthcare professionals in England to an IT spine, providing a care-records service, electronic booking of hospital appointments (Choose and Book), picture archiving and communications systems (PACS) and electronic transmission of prescriptions. And its goal was to enable...well what? It was a transformational IT project without a transformed service vision to support.

Sure, it had the goal of a national shared patient record, but no-one worked out why that was needed and how it would be used to deliver better care. Giving doctors access to the records of someone taken ill while on holiday was the headline.

Do I think a shared record is a bad idea? No, if it is associated with the changes needed to take advantage of it. I remember talking to a senior supplier of the NPfIT who told me that the goal of the programme was to create an online patient record. Why, I asked? I am still waiting for an answer—though you can't blame a supplier for helping to deliver what it was contracted for.

Though NPfIT did not achieve its main goal of a cross-organisational record, some good did come from it: digital radiology images (PACS); the renewal of a national data network; IT systems to support Cinderella areas of the NHS like community and mental health; a partly implemented summary-care record; shared patient demographics; a pattern for a comprehensive shared patient record adhering to standards; electronic transfer of prescriptions. Also—in a decade or so— it may also be recognised as the initiative that at last roused the clinical establishment to the potential of IT.

But an IT programme of that scale has a seismic effect on any organisation that will reveal the voids, cracks and fault lines. The lack of a coherent operational vision and with guaranteed increased funding doing little to incentivise new processes of care—meant the Programme's failure was pre-ordained.

Of course, I write with the benefit of twenty years of experience of healthcare IT and twenty:twenty hindsight. Nonetheless, I think Machiavelli 500 years after he wrote *Il Principe* would have recognised the dynamics at play. Let's face it, NPfIT was being asked to do what no political party would dare: to change the NHS radically.

GETTING THE CLINICIANS ON BOARD

Joseph-Marie Jacquard was a master silk-weaver in Napoleonic France. Jacquard invented a loom that accelerated the rate at which master weavers could create their exquisite fabric by twenty five times. The loom stored patterns and instructions for the beautiful designs on punched cards— an innovation that Charles Babbage used to programme his Analytical Engine, the world's first computer.

The precursor of Jacquard's loom was the drawloom. Individual threads of the warp were lifted by it to create a path through which the shuttle was passed by a draw boy. The drawloom allowed patterns to be weaved at the unprecedented rate of two rows a minute. It was while I was reading *Jacquard's Web* by James Essinger, which describes how a development of a hand-loom led to the information age that an analogy occurred to me. This passage caught my eye:

'The real problem was that the drawloom was not a machine at all. Instead, it was only a device for facilitating the manual weaving of patterns or images in the fabric...'

Facilitating the manual weaving: that describes healthcare IT. It's an aid to care rather than an integral part of care with roughly the status of an abacus or a pocket calculator.

For years I have listened to Chief Executives, IT Managers, Civil Servants use the shibboleth that allows them to cross into the land of the IT cognoscenti: get the clinicians on board. Somewhere the value of user engagement had become plain to them, so it was necessary to engage a major IT user group—clinicians.

Now, I have personal experience of piles of cheese and biscuits and crates of red wine lying untouched in a lecture hall at a presentation of an electronic-patient-record IT system, when from an expected attendance of sixty hospital consultants, only a handful showed up. A recent article in the *Economist* (Dec 1 2012 pp10) referred to the medical establishment as 'infamous for its inertia'. Therefore, for me the first question is: why aren't clinicians already on board?

I first came to healthcare IT with a head full of full of ideas about quality management. In leading my first electronic patient-record programme in a London teaching hospital,

I found doctors warmish at the prospect of having easy access to transactional information, like letters, patient demographics, and diagnostic test results, but distinctly cool at the prospect of recording outcome information. Evidence-based healthcare should encourage the analysis of the relationship between process and outcome, but much clinical practice still seems to have no evidence base. Could the structure and recording that IT offers represent a cultural mismatch and therefore be one of the reasons for slow uptake of electronic records?

GP AUTOMATION

The other morning on the breakfast TV news, a Physiotherapist was interviewed about plans to allow podiatrists and physiotherapists to prescribe drugs to patients with long-term conditions. When asked how a prescriber could be sure that other medications the patient might be taking would not interact, the Physiotherapist gave the impression that the GP record, or an extract of it, would be available to refer to.

It's true England has a summary care record that shares some basic information between care settings. In some areas GPs even give other doctors read-access to the full electronic patient records. But the adoption of the summary care record across England is patchy.

In the UK all GPs have automated their practice, and information from their IT systems is used to manage the Quality and Outcomes Framework (QoF). For me, QoF has some way to go before it manages quality rather than process, but it is a good start.

GP systems have eliminated many routine tasks by using IT. Recently, I have been able to order repeat prescriptions by email and even to book an appointment online, and the present Minister of State for Health has urged doctors to make greater use of such simple applications as email and the Web. Sure, there is further to go in achieving greater patient benefits, but the rate of adoption by GPs when compared to other clinicians is praiseworthy in my estimation. Though this doesn't represent a revolution in care delivery, it can form the basis for integrating local care communities, something I'll discuss further later.

ENSLAVEMENT BY A SYSTEM

'I must create a system or be enslaved by another man's; I will not reason and compare: my business is to create.'
—William Blake.

William Blake's painting *Newton* hangs in Tate Britain in London. Newton looks like an automaton with a set of calipers that has sunk to the bottom of the sea. Here is someone who seeks the measure of everything, but the value of nothing, to misquote Oscar Wilde.

Rather like Blake, doctors have not taken to measurement and evidence in quite the way that might have been hoped. Ironically, lack of evidence is often used to challenge new practices, and sometimes, dare I say it, as a reason for not adopting them. One wonders, therefore, how medicine would have developed if it had not been for trailblazers prepared to take risks—like infecting themselves with *Helicobacter* to prove it was a cause of stomach ulcers—or promoting asepsis, both ideas resisted by the medical establishment.

Medicine seems in a state of indecision, not sure whether to wield science as a sword to seek the truth or to hold it as a shield to block progress. Asking for evidence that IT is effective is like asking for evidence that the telephone is a useful medium for talking to patients and colleagues, or indeed that our senses are an effective medium—after all they are processed by the subjective mechanism of our brains.

We live our lives moving forward in time and there are no data about what comes next. All data are historical. So taking the request for evidence to the extreme would mean we would never innovate, since we would have insufficient data. This circular logic seems to be associated with some of the lack of wholesale adoption of IT by clinicians.

But the inability to see beyond the limits of business-as-usual is common to all sectors and all professions, and it is certainly not unique to clinicians. What's more, it's a blessed relief after working in the field for twenty years, to see doctors actually using IT and being proponents of its use. GP automation is a step in the right direction, but that is what it is. We must not rest there when there is much further to go.

HEALTH INFORMATICS

Healthcare has a tendency to compartmentalise, and so it is with IT. Instead of integrating IT in the way that commerce, and indeed the rest of the world, has, healthcare has regarded it with suspicion and isolated and marginalised it.

But how is IT to be an integral if it is seen as something separate, to the extent of having a separate discipline named health informatics? After all, information-rich industries like finance and travel that would cease to function without IT systems have no similar disciplines.

I have three academic degrees myself, so I support the notion that some academic knowledge is a good thing. However, my wife studied Physiotherapy for a few years at a top medical school and was taught almost nothing that could be applied practically. The breach between academia and the real world is nowhere clearer than in healthcare IT. In academia, IT has been boxed and labelled where it can be controlled while the NHS gets on with the real work.

Moreover, I regularly hear the call that we must bring together the thinkers and doers in healthcare IT as though the two were mutually exclusive. Few of the major technical advances of the past would have taken place unless thinkers were also doers—think Edison, or in more recent times, James Dyson with his revolutionary vacuum-cleaner design.

Nor must we also assume that academics are better or clearer thinkers. Professor Richard Smith, editor of the *British Medical Journal* until 2004, said only about five percent of the entire planet's scientific papers came up to scratch. In most journals, he said, it was less than one percent. Indeed, most of the Health Informatics publications I have read fall into two categories: the bean counting variety best kept by the bedside as a soporific, and the rest: weak and subjective.

Health Informatics faces the same challenges as fields like sociology and psychology, which also depend highly on the interpretation of human behaviour, because the success or failure of healthcare IT is largely determined by how well users apply it. Fundamentally, IT is not something separate from healthcare, and it must become integrated with it until it is essentially invisible, rather than being something esoteric and disembodied.

MANAGERS AND IT

The slow pace of integration is, however, not down only to clinicians and academics. Managers and leaders, by being ignorant of the potential for information technology, are equally at fault. Most hospital boards have no technology expertise, with IT usually reporting to another executive director. Technology innovation rarely has a part in operational planning—a huge failing. The consequence of this will be all sorts of poor strategic decisions.

One of the first things I noticed when I first joined the NHS was that Information Systems were (and still are) regarded as something on the periphery, almost a necessary evil, which for an information-rich industry like healthcare is flabbergasting.

I was influenced by Professor Enid Mumford who worked at Manchester Business School investigating the human and organisational effects of computer systems. Rare among academics, she had gained practical experience by working in the personnel department of an aircraft manufacturer and as a production manager for a clock manufacturer.

She noticed the implementation of large computer systems often failed to produce expected outcomes even when the technology was sound. Other researchers reached similar conclusions and the phenomenon eventually became known as the 'IT Productivity Paradox'. Decades on, I still read research into healthcare that indicates the lack of benefits arising from the implementation of IT as a surprise. It is not.

Professor Mumford devised a design method named ETHICS—Effective Technical and Human Implementation of Computer-based Systems—to address this problem. Essentially, it has three objectives: fully engage users in design; set job-satisfaction objectives as well as technical and operational ones; and ensure technical systems are compatible with human systems. It is the last of these that is crucial. ETHICS regards technology as a means not an end; one factor in the creation of a high-quality work environment and improved efficiency.

Well, Professor Mumford's approach has fallen from favour and fashion, but the underlying principle is sound: good systems design is far more than good technical design; it also requires a design approach that covers technology and the organisational context in which the technology is placed. This implies the total redesign of departments, functions and areas, including roles, relationships, activities and jobs.

And there is some recognition of this. I took part in a planning seminar for an NHS Trust a few months ago, which was well attended by clinical staff. After agreeing the organisation's transformational priorities the group looked for the main enablers. I expected the usual confection of more consultants, more nurses and more money—but no. IT was seen as a key enabler.

IT is not a quick fix. Add an IT system to a mix of unchanged—and even poor—human processes, and we must expect costs to increase and quality standards to fall. This is especially the case if work-arounds have to be implemented, because the system doesn't support 'the way we do it here'. A better health system will not magically appear when the boxes are switched on.

LIMITATION OF *LEAN* AND OTHER CHANGE METHODS

In recent years the implementation of IT has been associated with the use of methods such as *Lean* and *Six Sigma*. *Lean* to reduce waste and *Six Sigma* to reduce variability and defects. Change managers have also had a bonanza, but without a burning platform as an incentive for the NHS to jump in and swim, the results have been modest. While the use of such methods is certainly a step in the right direction, most of the initiatives I have seen are mired in current thinking and lacking in radical innovation. So we end up by making obsolescent processes more efficient instead of looking for new, more effective solutions. But reduced funding, changing epidemiology and changed expectations are now fanning the flames licking the platform.

Patient outcomes must be paramount. I would endure poor organisation and dodgy processes if I were assured of the best outcome for my condition. But these kinds of outcome measure are still difficult to find and in many cases still not part of the prevalent medical culture. Many of the NHS 'outcome measures' are really process measures: how long did the patient wait; what was the patient's experience of the intervention; did we weigh them and measure their blood pressure?

The ascendency of risk management also acts as an inhibitor. Some NHS organisations have governance and risk departments that are larger than their IT departments. With such a critical mass, and the culture that accompanies it, the NHS risks being further mired in compliance—with the underlying assumption being that we know what to comply with. Such an attitude also inhibits innovation, because it is easier to tick a box than to think outside of it. Good governance and risk management are part of the proficient management of a well-designed system, not something separate.

In summary, the creation of a digital NHS will be no small challenge. But like all journeys, it will begin with the first step and that is with a vision.

SUMMARY

1. System change is difficult and also perilous for the person leading it.
2. The NHS National Programme for IT was an IT programme without a revised operational model to support. To be effective and efficient IT must be associated with changed structure and process.
3. Clinical engagement in change is seen as key. But clinicians have accepted structured themes like Evidence-Based Medicine and Care Pathways only slowly. IT is very good at supporting structure and in collecting and managing large volumes of information.
4. GP automation, using computers, is a step in the right direction but must not be seen as an endpoint—there is much further to go.
5. Seeking evidence must not be used to impede progress— there is scope for common sense and expert opinion. Indeed, a body of medicine is practiced without the underpinning of robust evidence already.
6. IT is an enabling technology and must become so integrated with care that is essentially invisible. Creating separate disciplines to manage healthcare IT might not be the best way to achieve this.
7. NHS managers are equally at fault. Technology is rarely represented on Boards and is only weakly considered in strategic planning.

8.   Success must be gauged on true measures of outcome. In this respect methods like Six Sigma and Lean are best used on changed systems to optimise them and cannot be relied upon to produce radical solutions.

9.   Being trapped by current thinking is common in all fields and disciplines but must be overcome to create new models of care.

CHAPTER THIRTEEN

VISION OF HEALTHCARE

'Where there is no vision the people perish...'
—Proverbs 29:18

Tomorrow's healthcare is not today's NHS. Tomorrow's healthcare is integrated, continuous, standardised, personalised and based on evidence and on prevention rather than cure. Therefore, we must not allow disruptive technologies like IT and genomics to be absorbed by the status quo and to deliver marginal improvements in effectiveness.

Nor must we lose the human touch. Tomorrow machines and humans do what each does best. Analogue empathy and digital precision are partners in the creation of this vision. The key is to escape from mindsets and to dare to create something new.

EVERYONE, ALL THE TIME

Second millennium processes are laughable—not to say indefensible—in this twenty-four-hour online world. Rather than an irksome adjunct, IT must become as invisible and integrated as pen and paper are now.

The world is seeded with computer chips and connected by wireless. Increasingly, wireless tags on objects and people will weave healthcare into a matrix of objects, customers and services that allow continuous access to everything, everywhere, all the time. Moreover, the IT applications that obsess the NHS now—like the electronic patient record, PACS, Pathology and Pharmacy—will simply be absorbed into this matrix. The future of healthcare IT in the NHS is one of centralised-information systems and devolved innovation.

WELLNESS SERVICE

The biggest change will be that the NHS will grow to encompass health and illness. Of course, we already have a split between public health and healthcare, but in the future the former will gain in prominence. I am not proposing that 'health' is forced upon us, because, as we shall see in a moment, personal control, choice and freedom must gain in prominence.

Future clinicians will have a comprehensive, continuous view of customers in real time. They will be able to see them, consult them and even watch the working of their internal organs. Remote monitoring can already monitor vital signs and warn of potential problems, such as overeating or lack of activity. It is possible for a person's whole life to be recorded and stored, not only for research, but to support proactive intervention.

Convergence devices, like smartphones, will remind you to get up and exercise after staring at a screen and will monitor vital signs, like heart rate, respiration, skin humidity. Through technology, the NHS's founding aim of providing a cradle-to-grave service can be a realised. Imagine a service that helps you to live your life in health rather than live until you are ill.

Medical Home Centres in the US are designed to offer ongoing and whole-person care, supported by evidence and clinical decision support. These organizations—of which there are a few, such as Kaiser Permanente—are structured to profit from members' wellness, rather than their sickness. Personalised care using genetic makeup can augment such services to deliver a personalised service in wellness.

If this is too visionary for you, note it becomes clearer each day that older customers with multiple diseases are not a good fit to today's NHS. Usually these customers join a game of pass the patient between primary, acute and social care that reaches a climax when they slide down the slope through the emergency department into an expensive acute hospital bed. Moreover, managing the care of these customers with more expensive, specialized experts will rapidly become unaffordable. Leadership for the care of these patients in also unclear. If you have any doubt about this, try working with carers and NHS frontline staff. Let's hope leadership will become clearer as the new GP-led care commissioning groups come to grips with their role

ORGANISATION

'You never change things by fighting the existing reality. To change something, build a new model that makes the existing model obsolete.'
—Buckminster Fuller

Healthcare is an information science and its institutions are now looking like analogue artifacts in a digital age. Future

---

healthcare dispenses with organisations and structures that are really separated by a common goal. IT is indifferent to organisational boundaries. It can connect me with someone in an entirely different organisation in another part of the world as easily as it connects me to someone a few offices away. Organisations and boundaries are human constructs.

The biggest challenge—perhaps the most intractable— is for the NHS to escape the structure and processes that have constrained it since its inception. Its customers are not collections of specialties or customers of social, community or acute care. They are people with complex characters and needs and their health should be managed accordingly, rather than as a collection of ailments and interventions represented by a cost to one institution or another. To misquote Guy de Occam: care systems should not be multiplied unnecessarily.

History often shows technological disruptions are invented by existing institutions but are rarely used by them to create new operational models. New models are almost always created by new entrants. This is a worry to those enamoured of a publically-owned health service. Might customers be drawn from an obsolescent service to a newer more efficient one? To avoid this requires change on a scale the NHS has never before attempted.

QUEST FOR EFFICIENCY

As I write, the NHS strives to save money using a variety of tactics: outsourcing back-office functions; integration of primary care into triage units at secondary care A&E departments; closer working with community care; faster discharge and better bed management. The latest panacea is the take-over of smaller organisations by larger ones—and so it goes on. These may produce short-term savings. But the National Audit Office says the NHS will soon exhaust quick wins like these and will then struggle to meet the savings targets it has been set.

The benefit of quick wins is that they teach the NHS to manage without the mending machine of increased funding that it enjoyed before the credit crunch. The disbenefit is in trying to force a health model well past its retirement date to operate more efficiently—rather like flogging a horse to greater efforts while a steam engine—let alone a computer—idles nearby.

ADDRESSING DEMAND

The NHS must create an entirely new concept that concentrates on stemming demand by dealing with it more efficiently and economically. By keeping customers healthy and by helping people with long-term conditions to avoid expensive secondary and inpatient care it achieves this. Two of the biggest changes to healthcare will be a greater emphasis on prophylaxis and the more effective management of long-term conditions. We must reduce our use of the backstop of an acute hospital bed for those with long-term conditions. Hospital stays for such patients account for about half of the cost of the NHS. By avoiding a stay, we can avoid about £500 per day per patient.

We have seen how IT and genetics may help us to keep patients healthy. But we also need new operating models that are incentivised to keep people out of an illness service. This suggests a greater emphasis on what we now call public health—and history supports that. By emphasising prevention rather than cure, sewers, vaccination, better housing and clean water have contributed more to health than the whole of medical practice. Local councils, who manage public health, also have a greater understanding of general health issues, and have been far more active in applying technology like remote care to support the elderly and infirm—and this has been incentivised through government grants.

MERGING

One of the biggest changes to NHS, social and third-sector care will be the move away from fixed locations. Partly, as a consequence of this, organisational boundaries will be fluid. Future care is virtual and networked.

A paper-record and book-centric mindset has led to a fractured form of care that it is location and expert dependent. Therefore, one of the biggest changes is the merging of primary and secondary care in the NHS with social and third-sector care. IT promotes integrated networks of care that rely on the input of a variety of experts and of the patients themselves. The model is already there—recall social media.

Further, the greater use of social media opens the possibility of customers managing their own illness. My view is the best person to manage your health is you. Fellow suffers—or even the worried well—can lend each other support and can share experiences of what has, and what has not, worked for them.

In today's terms, the creation of a networked model will require the integration of social and NHS services. For example, in the care of the aged to support them in independent living, there will need to be new monitoring and new delivery mechanisms.

A possible funding mechanism for this is suggested by *Patientslikeme*, which offers research on people with real life co-morbidities, rather than the controlled environment in which treatments are normally tested. This is not as inimical to public-sector care as it sounds, because some NHS hospitals are already marketing anonymised data to Pharma.

What is also clear is that the management of long-term conditions lacks clear lines of accountability and leadership. A networked model allows care to be co-ordinated and for leaders to easily measure the performance of their organisations against performance measures and service levels. Desired performance can also be incentivized.

General Practice finds itself at a crossroads. The general tendency in the greater use of IT is to squeeze out the middleman, so the traditional role of the GP as gatekeeper is at risk. Moreover, the majority of a GP's workload is associated with the management of long-term conditions, for which I have proposed a more effective networked model.

These considerations can be seen as a threat or as an opportunity. GPs can risk their role being marginalized or they can take the lead in creating new models focused on the management of long-term conditions or on the treatment of standardized conditions.

~

PERIL OF AGGREGATION

The latest *plat du jour* is for larger organisations to take over smaller ones. This allows some economies of scale—such as a reduction in management and so-called back-office costs. But by this ingestion, processes remain unchanged. Further, bigger organisations will make it increasingly difficult to analyse, disaggregate and establish more economical care models. Bigger operational model, same processes, same problems. Aggregation is in exactly the wrong direction.

Other initiatives may bolster services with twenty-four-hour non-emergency cover, thereby making better use of expensive NHS resources like theatres and imaging equipment. On the face of it this sounds like a good fit with customer expectations of a continuous service; but the marginal costs like staff and consumables must be funded and bottlenecks, like the availability of inpatient beds, cleared. Moreover, we have seen that additional funding into pre-existing structure and process is unlikely to increase efficiency—and will therefore add cost.

Without question, the need for centres of expertise for diagnosis and emergency care will remain, but their size and scope will be pared down. As soon as diagnosis and treatment can be tightly yoked, care can be standardised and migrated to more efficient operational models. This flies in the face of the current trend for larger organisations to ingest smaller ones . A better trend would be for large organisations to retain specialist services while divesting of commoditised services to the smaller fish.

LOCAL SOLUTIONS

Standardisation and commoditisation of care into new models of care comes close to the proposals made by Professor the Lord Darzi of Denham when he reviewed NHS care in London. He suggested eighty percent of local surgery could be carried out in health centres and large GP practices. He wanted to separate off routine surgery that could be carried out in localised polyclinics rather than in gargantuan London institutions.

Lord Darzi's plans proceeded to some extent but were resisted by all sorts of interested groups, a phenomenon that will befall any change to the system, as we have seen. Everyone agrees that the NHS needs reform; no-one agrees how that should be accomplished. It is also true that dispersed centres depend on good public transport—which of course London has—an argument often deployed against local health centres in other locations. I think there is some validity in this argument, though it does not represent an insurmountable difficulty and has more than a whiff of resistant, present thinking about it.

It is also noteworthy that Lord Darzi's own research has included looking at how technology can be used in health-care delivery including the use of remote-presence robots and robotic surgery. Unfortunately his views now seem now to have fallen from vogue.

PATIENT POWER

An expert-centric care will resolve to a patient-centric system with the patient firmly in control of information flows. Social networking has made customers accustomed to sharing personal information with whom they choose. Therefore, the digital generation will question the need for medical records controlled by a third party, let alone a specific group of that third party. Furthermore, patient control will lead to a far more comprehensive record than a doctor can accumulate in a lifetime of sporadic consultation.

With medical information online at a tap, the digital generation will challenge the more creative aspects of medical practice and seek evidence and social confirmation online. Increasing volumes of data that relate treatment to real outcome will become available leading to the benchmarking of the competence of organisations—and individual practitioners—both of which will be easily shared with other consumers. We already have the blunt measure of mortality rates, but measures will grow in number and in sophistication.

GENETICS, SNPS AND MUTABILITY

The *Facebook* generation will expect care to be focused on its needs. Mutability is a feature of web applications—they reform content based on activity, interests and perceived needs. They also react quickly—note how your *Facebook* pages alter their composition according to your recent activity. Further, lifestyle data can be collected easily from social media giving a greater range and number of variables than ever.

But these are historical data. To some extent we may also be gifted with foresight. Your genome may offer clues to your future health allowing mitigation and maybe even prevention. Genetics also offers the basis of stratification using specific genetic differentiators—like Single Nucleotide Polymorphisms. Since there are multiple SNPs, care will not be fully personalized, but the combination of lifestyle, treatment and outcome data will allow care to be targeted in the general population as never before.

VOLUME OF DATA

IT use generates huge volumes of data. As we have noted, *Google* already knows more about you than your doctor. Furthermore, the combination of real-time data and genetic stratification opens the prospect of continual improvements to evidence-based care and continual feedback on the efficacy of practice.

Not only will clinicians will have far more information on proxy outcomes—such as complications and readmission rates—but they will be also be able to collect data on personalised outcomes related to genetic makeup. Medical nomenclature may also be redefined using genetic (or perhaps protein) markers rather than by physiological location.

SIMPLIFICATION AND STANDARDISATION

Few medical textbooks offer clear guidelines grounded in science about when a doctor should refer a patient suffering from a specific condition to a specialist, much less when it is appropriate to order a diagnostic or imaging test. This is particularly true for those nearing the end of life. Books offer no evidence-based clinical guidelines for how often doctors should schedule such patients for return visits; when they should be hospitalized or admitted to intensive care; or what palliative care they should receive.

That said, the NHS has developed the *Map of Medicine* that can be used to manage patient journeys and to optimise performance against key-performance measures. Its aim is to help health communities to improve care quality while reducing cost. I have already argued that the use of structured medicine is a key benefit of the greater use of IT in health-care. What's more, evidence-suggests care pathways result in reduced length of stay and fewer complications. Regrettably, I worry that innovations such as this will be put to better use by non-NHS organisations which, as Clayton Christensen suggests, is historically how innovative operational models are exploited.

~

Human practitioners have free will. Surrounded by a pile of policies, procedures, best-practice guidelines and tick boxes, they decide whether to follow them or not. The simple fact is people can make a perfect system succeed or fail.

On the other hand, technology can be completely controlled—we program it after all. Therefore, the key to efficiency and a reduction in wasteful variability is the standardisation of process using IT. Pathways of care and the collection of knowledge can be codified using comprehensive health languages like SNOMED CT—or perhaps future languages that are based on molecular markers. In addition, IT systems are much better at carrying out systematised tasks time after time without becoming bored, emotional or even a little bit off-colour.

In turn, this permits the migration of tasks from highly-skilled experts to generalists. Nurse practitioners and assistants will do work once performed by doctors. What's more, care can be standardized and carried out by experienced staff comparably and economically.

If to some experts more structure means 'tick-box medicine' to reduce errors, so what? There will be plenty of work for experts. The cost of encoding expertise is high. For example, a well-known medical journal employs about sixty staff who read and grade research. Their output is then reviewed by a team of clinicians, before being encoded, published and distributed.

When expertise can be encoded into software, such as Expert Systems, it will be increasingly possible for it to be updated like the operating system on a PC upgrades itself in the background. In this manner, changes to best practice can be distributed easily and need less policing by organisations such as NICE, GMC and CQC. To most clinicians this will require a move away from the top-down, expertise-led approach to a form of healthcare that is based on outcomes and bottom-up feedback.

In a 1950 article in *Computing Machinery and Intelligence* Alan Turing argued that one day machines would think like humans. Turing suggested that we could consider a machine intelligent if its responses were indistinguishable from those of a human. This is the origin of the Turing Test.

With a standardisation of medical practice, the strength of the human practitioner grows in prominence. No machine is—or is ever likely to be—empathic. Perhaps a better redefinition of the Turing Test for healthcare might include the extent to which we can tell the difference between simulated machine empathy and human empathy. That test may never be successfully completed by a machine.

Greater use of decision support, like Expert Systems, will reduce the need for highly-trained doctors. Increasingly care will be passed to less highly-trained staff. Does this presage the end of the doctor? Not likely. Experts will have an increasing role in the assessment and codification of best practice—and in keeping it up-to-date.

US DEPARTMENT OF VETERANS AFFAIRS

The NHS is facing a challenge similar to that faced by the US Department of Veterans Affairs. In a relatively short period this declining, publically-funded, organization—whose buildings were run down, even rat-infested, and that was close to being wound up—has transfigured and is now able to boast that it provides 'the best care anywhere'. Not only that, but it has improved care quality while reducing cost—something rarely heard of in healthcare.

Ken Kizer served as the Under Secretary for Health in the United States Department of Veterans Affairs and is credited for the improvement in the VA healthcare delivery system in the 1990s. The changes Kizer made are not rocket science. They are just good management, applied to healthcare, led by a determined person with a vision.

On taking the job, Kizer created the vision of a new structure, with new processes and new people. Before he arrived the VA was considered a hospital service. During his time in office, it was transformed into a care service offering measurable, comprehensive and high-quality care. The hospital-centric service was converted into twenty-two integrated networks and the use of hospital beds was reduced by fifty percent.

Leaders of this integrated care service were held accountable for performance goals—mainly based on the quality of care. Performance was regularly revised and compared to that of other services. Underpinning this transformation were integrated IT systems that included an Electronic Patient Record and extensive use of telehealth.

The VA maintains a life-long relationship with its customers—rather like healthcare in the UK. So it takes a long-term view of health; for example, in realising that failure to manage diabetes at an early stage only results in more cost and poorer outcomes later. The VA considers cost and quality in relation to a whole care system and to a whole patient. Therefore, investment in integrated IT systems could only be to its advantage.

There was also one important industry structural factor: the VA had flourishing private-sector competition. Though public concern about the imminent privatisation of the NHS is regularly stoked by the news media no matter which government is in power, you have to ask whether some competition might not, after all, be beneficial.

That said, Kizer was subject to far less political interference than would be the case in the NHS, and he had more control over some powerful interest groups like service providers and contractors—thereby lessening the likelihood of organizational dynamics interfering. Nonetheless, the transformation of the VA offers the NHS at least three lessons.

First, consider acute hospitals as costs and fund them in proportion to the population they serve. The reduction in bed use achieved by the VA suggests the NHS has more to do in integrating care, thereby reducing the need for expensive inpatient stays.

Second, the creation of integrated-care networks. The VA budgeted for these also according to the size of the population they served, making the use of acute care an undesirably expensive option if better care could be provided elsewhere in the integrated system.

Third, the implementation of an extensive integrated patient-record that generates hard figures to measure cost, quality and performance. Note the VA did not invest large sums and time in looking for the evidence for this common-sense investment. Many of us living in the UK would like to experience the so-called *Duracell*® Effect—that is we run and run before dying after a short illness. This for me is the consummate outcome goal of twenty-first century healthcare.

STOP SAVING THE NHS

Clayton Christensen, in *The Innovator's Prescription*, and Buckminster Fuller, whose quotation begins this chapter, suggest the solution to the NHS's problems lies outside of its institutions. To avoid proving them both right and making the continual warnings of imminent NHS privatisation self-fulfilling, needs radical change.

If we pursue delaying tactics, like seeking evidence for common-sense practices, change could take decades. We don't have that long. The time for action is not after we have run yet another research pilot that benefits only academics and leads to uncertain conclusions that require (you guessed it) more research. Nor is more time needed to find the evidence related to the use of IT. The examples of UK General Practice and the US Department of Veterans Affairs are enough for anyone.

The key to success at the VA was that IT underpinned a complete revision of the delivery model. Moreover, the VA has shown that costs can be controlled and quality standards raised by a combination of changed structure, process and IT.

While thinking about this, I watch from my office window a girl of about six with her mother dragging her way to school, completely absorbed by a mobile phone. The Digital Generation has never known a world without computers, that's why some call them screen babies. To them IT *just is*, and so it should be in healthcare. Today's NHS is an anachronism. Health services should (and will) be delivered on phones, notepads, televisions or whatever the fashionable convergence device is.

To survive, the NHS must become a harmonious blend of people, processes and technology. Options that defend the status quo are exhausted. Do you think the Digital Generation—let alone generation Y and even generation X— will accept the paper-fixated NHS? I mean *really*?

Those fighting for revision often see only part of the process, which they try to reform. But to achieve what I have described requires wholesale revision. In the UK, few have dared this. The NHS National Programme for IT tackled it as a technology programme without an operational goal, and we saw the outcome. We need real, co-ordinated, vision-led change. Launching IT systems into unchanged structures and practices will achieve nothing—there is plenty of evidence in and outside healthcare of that. Setting an IT programme out alone to create wholesale change is setting out to fail.

Will people resist and be upset by the change I have proposed? Certainly. Creating a new system of care without upsetting someone is impossible. But, as Dr Johnson said, the prospect of being hanged focuses the mind wonderfully. Part of me thinks the time is right for wholesale change, and part of me thinks that powerful interests will make it impossible. To them I say: please stop saving the NHS and start reinventing it.

SUMMARY

1. Future healthcare is a combination of human and machine: analogue empathy and digital precision. The fragmented paper-based NHS will grate increasingly with the world outside. NHS organisations are looking like analogue artifacts in a digital age.

2. Advances in genetics and computing have made Medicine an information science.

3. The NHS will become a true health service supporting you to live in health rather than live until you are ill. This will reduce the demand for expensive hospital services. Further, an older patient suffering from multiple diseases is not a customer best matched to the current NHS, and the evidence for that increases daily.

4. A migration from an institutional mindset to one that allows more focused care in specialist elective care and minor-injuries units is likely. Therefore, the trend to aggregation seeking economies of scale is exactly the wrong thing to do.

5. Greater use of decision support, like Expert Systems, will further reduce the need for expensive doctors. When diagnosis and treatment can be tightly related, care can be commoditised and carried out at scale with less expert and less expensive staff. However, experts will have a growing role in the assessment and codification of best practice.

6. Reduced use of acute and hospital care is essential if care is to be affordable. Large institutions are still needed for the diagnosis and the management of less precise medicine and to manage emergency care.

7. General Practice is at a crossroads. It can risk being left behind as most of its activity in the management of long-term conditions migrates to more effective models, or it can take the lead.

8. Patients will increasingly take charge of their own health—particularly their own records—and will use the Internet and social media to challenge practitioners.

9. Personal health monitoring and the personalisation of care using genetic markers is a reality that people will increasingly choose to remain healthy.

10. As IT takes over routine, doctors will be increasingly valued for their human qualities rather than their ability to memorise and infer like machines.

11. IT will become so integrated into care that it will be essentially invisible. No longer will it be seen as something different from the art of medicine.

12. The US Department of Veterans Affairs has demonstrated that a publically-funded organisation can change its structure, adopt major IT, reduce cost and improve the quality of care using nothing more than clear, determined leadership and good management practice.

13. People will be upset and the path will be difficult, but if the NHS is to survive we need to stop saving it and start reinventing it.

FOR MORE INFORMATION

Please also visit *www.stopsavingthenhs.com* or
www.kineticconsulting.co.uk. In addition, I post on
Twitter about health and technology: *@colin_jervis.*

REFERENCES

Christensen, Clayton M (2009) *The Innovators Prescription: a disruptive solution for healthcare.* McGraw Hill, New York

Dixon, Patrick (2007) *Futurewise: six faces of global change.* Profile Books, London

Essinger, James (2007) *Jacquard's Web.* OUP, Oxford

Forster, EM (1909) *The Machine Stops.* (Can be read here: *http://archive.ncsa.illinois.edu/prajlich/forster.html.* Also a 1966 BBC film adaptation: *http://www.youtube.com/watch?v=kvrGUnIFuRs*)

Gall, John (2006) *The Systems Bible.* General Systemantics Press, New York

Kaku, Michio (2011) *Physics of the Future: How Science Will Shape Human Destiny and Our Daily Lives by the Year 2100.* Penguin

Kessler, Andy (2006) *End of Medicine.* Collins, New York

Longman, Phillip (2012) *Best Care Anywhere: Why VA Health Care Would Work Better For Everyone.* (Bk Currents Book) Berrett-Koehler Publishers.

Prof. Robert Winston and Prof. Noel Sharkey interview on BBC Radio 4: *http://news.bbc.co.uk/today/hi/today/newsid_7574000/7574056.stm*

Tang H, Ng J. *Googling for a diagnosis – use of Google as a diagnostic aid: internet based study.* BMJ 2006;333:1143-1145

ABOUT THE AUTHOR

After travelling the world working for multi-national companies in marketing, Colin Jervis changed careers and has worked in and around the NHS and healthcare for twenty years. During that time he led three major IT transformational change programmes in the NHS. He has also worked with healthcare organisations in the USA, Europe and the Middle East and is a popular chair, speaker and workshop leader. He now works as a management and healthcare consultant.

He has three academic degrees including masters in business administration and business systems analysis and design. He has many published articles and has been interviewed by the Financial Times and Telegraph about his work. In his spare time he keeps fit, draws and looks after three cats. He has loved science and art since discovering a book of Leonardo's anatomical drawings in his local library as a child.

27741903R00092

Printed in Great Britain
by Amazon